The power of one, the power of many

First published March 2009

NHS Institute for Innovation and Improvement:
Jo Bibby*
Helen Bevan
Elizabeth Carter

The Medical School, University College London:
Paul Bate
Glenn Robert*

* Jo Bibby is now Director of Improvement Programmes at the Health Foundation
* Glenn Robert is now Senior Research Fellow, National Nursing Research Unit

FOREWORD

▷ ## Social movement thinking: a set of ideas whose time has come?

We have reached a seminal point in our health and healthcare improvement efforts.

Across the globe, many leaders have transformational ambitions for health and healthcare services. The key issue is not whether the potential for safer, more effective care exists, but how to realise that potential across the entire system for every citizen, every service user and every patient. Are the improvement strategies and approaches that have got us to where we are today enough to deliver that different future?

Most ideas that underpin contemporary healthcare improvement are derived from 'planned' or 'programmatic' approaches to change. Within the English National Health Service (NHS), the last 10 years has seen a multitude of improvement programmes and projects, initiated at both local and national level and often with impressive results. However, there is recognition that, on their own, projects and programmes will not deliver the radical and far-reaching changes that are required. In addition to changing structures and processes within healthcare, we need to embrace new sorts of thinking and fresh perspectives to get better, faster, more sustainable results.

"As healthcare leaders, we need the courage to make a personal stand for what is right. We need to make a profound connection with the deep-seated values that brought us and our colleagues into healthcare in the first place"

The ideas and experiences in this report represent nearly seven years of work by the NHS Institute for Innovation and Improvement, its predecessor organisation – the NHS Modernisation Agency – and our academic partners from the Medical School, University College London.

This has been a highly-inclusive process involving hundreds of NHS clinicians and leaders, policy makers, improvement practitioners and social movement researchers from across the world. Feedback has been remarkable. People are genuinely excited about the potency of these ideas and they are already making a difference for scores of local healthcare teams and their patients.

Our work with local NHS teams suggests that a social movement perspective may help to reinvigorate and redefine both large-scale improvement efforts and local front-line change initiatives alike. Social movement thinking is about connecting with people's core values and motivations, and mobilising their own personal energies and drivers for change. This viewpoint is underpinned by solid evidence from the change management field that people change what they do less because they are given an analysis that shifts their thinking, and more because they are shown a truth that influences their feelings.

The social movement perspective fundamentally challenges the ways we have learnt to organise and lead change in the NHS. As healthcare leaders, we need the courage to make a personal stand for what is right. We need to make a profound connection with the deep-seated values that brought us and our colleagues into healthcare in the first place. We need to challenge the status quo as necessary and tackle the tough issues head on. At the root of it all, we have to believe that a different future is possible, and that the people we work with and serve have the capability, energy and motivation to deliver the changes.

"Before I became involved in the NHS social movements work, I often saw myself as an activist outside of my professional life, but applied very different tactics and a different mindset in my NHS role"

At various times in my life, I have been an active contributor to social movements and campaigns. Before I became involved in the NHS social movement work, I often saw myself as an activist outside of my professional life, but applied very different tactics and a different mindset in my NHS role.

The most important lesson I have learnt from this social movement initiative is that, as improvement leaders, we need to be activists in our work lives as much, or even more, than in any other sphere of our lives. Our great mission of high quality care for all requires the same passion, commitment and mass participation as any other movement cause.

Whether you are a clinician in a front-line patient care role; a trade union activist, or a Chief Executive, I hope you will be energised and inspired by the ideas and experiences in this report.

Given the emerging NHS themes of population-based health, localisation, grass roots engagement and individual and community empowerment, perhaps this is a set of ideas whose time has come.

Helen Bevan
Chief of Service Transformation
NHS Institute for Innovation and Improvement

CONTENTS

EXECUTIVE SUMMARY

The Power of One, the Power of Many makes a powerful case for the way in which social movement thinking can be incorporated into existing health and healthcare improvement practice to create more effective, compelling, faster change for patients and the public. The essence of the report is how social movement approaches – based on connecting with peoples' core values and motivations to affect change – can deliver improvement at previously unseen depths.

But it is not just an issue of connecting with values. It is about helping people to see themselves as leaders of change, organising change in ways that create commitment and mass participation and keeping the momentum going by helping people to stay engaged for the long-term.

The publication represents almost seven years of research by the NHS Institute for Innovation and Improvement alongside academic partners from the Medical School, University College London. The process has involved hundreds of NHS clinicians, leaders and policy makers, improvement practitioners and social movement researchers from across the globe.

Most ideas that underpin contemporary health and healthcare improvement are derived from 'planned' or 'programmatic' approaches to change. However, there is recognition that, on their own improvement projects and programmes do not always deliver the radical and far-reaching changes required for the longer term. Some additional thinking is needed. The Power of One, the Power of Many provides an accessible package which sets out these complementary approaches to change in a compelling way. It includes case studies of social movement approaches being used in healthcare settings, which will give readers confidence in using these approaches themselves.

The report begins by recording views of NHS health improvement leaders about their experiences, hopes and aspirations. These suggest that there is often a disconnection between front-line staff and the way that the values of their organisations are lived out in reality. The concept of The Power of One, the Power of Many is highlighted with the case study of David Shier, an English General Practitioner. The 'Early Psychosis Declaration' was issued by the World Health Organisation as a result of David's experience of his teenage daughter's mental illness and what was felt to be her effectively being 'written off' by the apparatus of social / mental healthcare. The 'declaration' sets out five key objectives for action to provide young people who develop psychosis with access to quality mental health services and social intervention. This story is analysed to highlight core characteristics which suggest that every one of us has the potential to be an active 'change agent' even if like David, there is an initial reluctance to do so. In the second chapter, A new way of thinking, the authors tackle the question of how to translate social movement thinking into the NHS and draws parallels with the challenges faced by past movements and their progress including: social, labour, religious, environmental and civil rights movements. Seven core characteristics of social movements are defined. The mainstreaming of the environmental movement illustrates how social movements has become a major field of research today and the authors make the case for its applicability to healthcare.

The authors go on to explore how a social movement approach differs from a traditional programmatic approach; how a movement view of change differs from our current view, and what the difference is between organisational logic and 'movements consciousness'. The Power of One, the Power of Many analyses the dynamics of the energy focus of social movement. It contrasts this with the predominant 'efficiency and effectiveness' focus within healthcare improvement through various illustrative analogies, including right brain / left brain thinking. The authors advocate a holistic approach which recognises that there will be tensions between them and finding ways of negotiating these.

In chapter three: The case for social movements, the authors address the sceptics and present evidence from local healthcare teams that 'field tested' the social movement principles. The report illustrates how movement thinking is not incompatible with the concept of organisations. This evidence comes from field test teams who trialled social movement ideas for 'proof of concept'. It goes on to present the results of a 'polarity map' exercise undertaken with the test teams which shows reactions of the teams and how various aspects of activity 'sit' between positive and negative interaction between two schools of 'planned programmatic' and 'movement' approaches to change, and between 'Ideal future: Large scale sustainable improvement for patients' and 'Fears: Unable to deliver changes for patients'. The section closes with five key principles for creating social movement dynamics within an organisation.

The fourth chapter: Change as a personal mission, profiles the essential qualities of movement 'activists'. It describes how those in leadership roles, whether formal organisational roles or informal roles can incorporate social movement ideas into their leadership practice. The section provides some 'rules of thumb' for activists to 'stay alive' by managing the risks associated with the role.

The authors present a number of examples including the results of a workshop exercise where NHS improvement leaders completed 'activists' CVs' and a group of infection control link practitioners explored their 'activist' roles in ways that gave them insight into how they could get their message across and influence others more powerfully.

In chapter five, Frame to connect with hearts and minds, the authors look at the concept of framing – the 'single most important principle of social movement thinking'. Framing is the process by which a movement leader or activist puts their cause across successfully to potential recruits by framing it in a way that connects with the core values and life experiences of the potential recruit This is illustrated with an outline of key approaches to effective framing. Successful and unsuccessful examples of framing are highlighted using a wide range of mediums from slogans and visual images to performances, events and spectacle, spanning political causes and satire-driven pressure campaigns such as those created by Michael Moore.

Chapter six, Energise and mobilise, explores how to get people to 'step off the pavement' and shift from bystander to activist. The authors outline how 'mobilisation' is a step beyond engagement and consider what a 'mobilised' healthcare organisation looks like. This section outlines approaches to energising and mobilising to release energy and harness it, illustrated by a case study of two midwives who took part in the first field test of the social movement approach.

The authors discuss how commitment and connection can be built and highlight the importance in mobilising narratives, such as 'authentic voices' and 'hot-housing', which can be used to forge deeper commitment. This is illustrated with high profile examples, such as Jamie Oliver's 'School Dinners' campaign to show how this was used to 'build mass'.

The chapter goes on to focus on healthcare campaigns, concluding with an overview of the concept of the 'tipping point' and its three key factors: the power of the few; the 'stickiness' of the message and the power of context.

For a movement to survive, activists must be able to create an enduring organisational structure to sustain collective action. In chapter seven, Organise for impact, the authors outline how most movements are underpinned by highly effective organisation.

This section outlines the 'movement' view of organisations and the key characteristics of organisations broken down into 'traditional tactics' and 'movement tactics'. It goes on to describe some key approaches to successful organising – campaign infrastructures and how networks operate as organising structures with different membership levels.

The authors outline what makes an effective leader and how to create an effective strategy for the organisational context, including movement tactics and 'rules for radicals'.

Chapter eight, Keep forward momentum, outlines the importance of the final principle of social movement: how to maintain momentum for long-term and continual improvement for healthcare organisations.

Evidence is drawn from a variety of successful social movements and healthcare examples and outlines the findings of social movement thinkers on campaigns, movements and their sustainability.

The final chapter, In closing, highlights the remaining challenge of fully integrating social movement thinking into healthcare. The authors outline the NHS Institute's plans for future social movement work and resource development to translate these powerful concepts and ideas into strategies and 'how to' tactics.

The Power of One, the Power of Many concludes: "..the movement approach is not something that can be meaningfully 'taught' in a technical way; rather it is something to be experienced, with people using the ideas themselves in order to become competent in facilitating others."

1. STARTING FROM A DIFFERENT PLACE

▶ 1.1 Background to this document

To-date, the prevalent approach to improvement in the English National Health Service (NHS) has been nationally initiated, programme-by-programme and focused on the achievement of performance targets. Most ideas that underpin this NHS improvement model have been taken from mainstream organisation studies; a discipline which encompasses organisational development, quality improvement, individual and team development and other approaches to change.

The NHS Plan (Department of Health, 2000) set out a transformational programme for the NHS. In the nine years since its publication, it has spawned a multitude of different, and often impressive, improvement schemes and activities. In 2008, the latest NHS blueprint for radical change, *High Quality Care for All*, set the bar even higher with its ambitious goals for population health and a focus on quality as the basic operating principle of the NHS. Estimates suggest that perhaps 15 to 20% of NHS staff are actively engaged in quality improvement work – a startling number given a total workforce of 1.3 million. Yet, achievement of the goals of *High Quality Care for All* may require 80 or 100% staff engagement. How will this happen? Should the number of NHS improvement projects be quadrupled? Or are some different, additional ways of thinking required? Evidence from the social sciences suggest that other perspectives may help us see large-scale organisational change efforts in a new light, offering us fresh, though complementary, approaches to improvement thinking and practice.

The aim of this report is to share some of these new approaches. It should be noted that these additional ideas are not intended to replace current methods, but rather to add to them, with the aim of delivering a depth and scale of improvement that we have not previously achieved in the NHS.

In essence, these approaches are about:

• individual courage, commitment and determination
• connecting with the values that people believe in
• unleashing energy and mobilising people
• translating that energy into purposeful action
• building a deep sense of community and the shared commitment needed to sustain improvements.

While not all of the ideas are new, their full potential in the NHS is yet to be realised.

This report sets out the thinking and evidence-base for this new approach to change. It is supplemented by a range of practical tools and tactics for translating theory into action.

You can find further details of many of the resources and ideas discussed in this document at: www.institute.nhs/socialmovements

1.2 The context

When NHS improvement leaders are asked about their experiences, hopes and aspirations for the NHS, we find many examples of people feeling passionate about the NHS or a specific local cause, demonstrating a personal connection to the drive to improve services for patients, carers and staff.

In the fifth annual national survey of NHS staff (conducted between October and December, 2007) almost 156,000 employees from all 391 NHS trusts in England responded to a questionnaire asking about their views and experiences of working for the NHS (Healthcare Commission, 2008). As figure 3 shows, only two-fifths (39%) of staff were satisfied with the recognition they get, and only a quarter (26%) said that they were satisfied, or very satisfied, with the extent to which the trust valued their work. This emerges as the single most common reason given by those thinking of leaving their jobs.

Something that lights a fire in my belly...

- When you see things not working
- Poor quality patient care
- When I see increasing failure
- Modernising HRM practices, showing managers a different way of doing things
- Strategic imperative to have Welfare State long-term
- When things go wrong for patients and staff
- Lost inhibitions
- Putting problems right
- Freedom to act
- When I see we have failed in patient care
- Seeing a problem/challenge and knowing what can be done differently
- When I see patients or staff not receiving good standards
- Identifying areas that can be changed
- Knowing that everyone in the NHS wants to give the best they can and make a difference
- Progress, change
- Seeing impact that small improvements can make to patients' experience
- People who do not perform or who are against change
- Seeing something that is wrong

- Hearing: 'That's how things are always done'
- When it is obvious the current system is not delivering good patient care
- I was/am a user of mental health services.
- I know what it is like to wait for services
- When the team is working together
- Vision of the future and how it could be better
- When the public/media have misconceptions about the NHS and what can be done
- Want to communicate a greater understanding
- When people tell me it cannot be done
- Other people's energy – lack of using it
- When I can see an opportunity to do something different to improve clinical patient outcomes
- To give support to it
- Seeing injustice, inequality and unfairness
- Justice and seeing people's needs are met (servant leadership)
- When it is said it cannot be done
- Seeing poor customer service
- The patient's experience

Figure 1: *What NHS improvement leaders are saying*

1. STARTING FROM A DIFFERENCE PLACE

Over the past three years, more than 700 NHS staff have taken part in an 'Organisational Energy Index™' survey, conducted by Stanton Marris Ltd as part of the social movement initiative (Stanton Marris, 2008).

While a sample of 700 people cannot be considered as representative of the entire NHS workforce, the fact that they have come from a range of NHS organisations and job levels, and that the results are consistent, is of interest. 'Connection with the organisational values' of the NHS was cited by respondents as a greater source of organisational energy than any other factor. The greatest sapping of organisational energy was the extent to which NHS organisations failed to live up to and deliver these values on a day-to-day basis (Stanton Marris, 2008).

What makes me angry and impatient for change?

- Targets and performance measures - their bluntness means the underneath improvement can get lost
- When dealing with complaints when we have failed – Hand-holding culture – cost reduction focused
- Lose sight as an organisation as to why we are here
- Lack of empowerment
- Poor standards becoming the norm
- Services not meeting basic needs
- When I can maintain my standards and see things around me done to a poor standard, or wastage
- Poor standards of practical patient care
- Site management will not shift
- When you/your team can see there is a better way of doing but you cannot get staff/management to see it your way
- Inefficient management systems. Too many parts to a whole that work differently
- Obstacles for the sake of it
- Bureaucracy, red tape, politics. Think through a situation differently to make a situation turn around positively
- Injustice
- Poor communication, doctors, patients, nurses
- When things are enforced
- Seeing wasted opportunities to involve and engage people, seeing disengagement

- People who say the right words but never act
- When others do not act (ask for forgiveness, not permission)
- Colleagues not listening or willing to change
- When reluctant to change, puts barriers up to improve things
- Poor practice being witnessed and challenge received with bad attitude
- When I see unnecessary failure
- 'Cannot do' attitude, compelled to act, actions of individuals affecting the team and patients
- When I have been positive hundreds of times and got very little in return
- When people are obstructive and difficult. I want to understand them and seek to explore and rectify
- When patients are not treated as individuals and staff do not care and are impatient in interactions with them
- When patients do not receive a good standard of care, e.g. poor discharge planning

Figure 2: *What NHS improvement leaders are saying*

Furthermore, at the annual NHS Confederation Conference in June 2008, 359 senior NHS leaders took part in an anonymous electronic vote on 'NHS values'. In response to the question: 'Does your organisation have an agreed set of values?', 37.6% said 'yes on paper'; 41.8% said 'yes and meaningful'; and 15.3% said 'no'. We would anticipate that senior NHS leaders would have a more positive view of organisational values than front-line staff, since they would typically have more responsibility for developing and demonstrating the values. The fact that nearly 60% of senior leaders stated that their organisation did not have meaningful values reinforces our own findings that there is a disconnection between front-line NHS staff and the values of their organisations.

Table 2.25: How satisfied are you with each of the following aspects of your job? Base: All staff	% satisfied or very satisfied		
	2005	2006	2007
The recognistion I get for good work	42%	41%	39%
The support I get from my immediate manager	58%	58%	57%
The freedom I have to choose my own method of working	64%	62%	61%
The support I get from work collegues	76%	75%	75%
The amount of responsibility I am given	70%	69%	68%
The opportunities I have to use my skills	64%	63%	64%
The extent to which my trust values my work	28%	27%	26%
My level of pay	-	-	29%

Figure 3: *How satisfied are you with aspects of your job survey*
Source: *National NHS staff surveys 2005, 2006, 2007*

1. STARTING FROM A DIFFERENCE PLACE

While it is clear that despite the achievement of some significant and truly remarkable system-wide improvements in the NHS, the biggest gains relate to the more predictable aspects of services – for example, waiting times and patient access which tend to arise from an instruction-based, command and control-type model of improvement.

This is not a surprise – prevailing improvement theories in healthcare have been drawn largely from industrial process improvement models. And yet we know that the delivery of a high-quality patient experience (and not simply an efficient process) is more challenging and require additional strategies that work in more complex environments like healthcare. These strategies need to reconnect organisational agendas to the values of frontline staff; involve those staff in improvement efforts; and then somehow find the energy to secure lasting change. It is the notion of recapturing the 'soul' of healthcare:

"The fact that nearly 60% of senior leaders stated that their organisation did not have meaningful values reinforces our own findings that there is a disconnection between front-line NHS staff and the values of their organisations"

"... about clawing back tender, loving healthcare, giving and receiving it, before we lose sight of what it is. It's about finding a way to restore the NHS to what it's there for; to rein in its spiralling complexity before it's too late. Bringing the healthcare debate back to where it belongs, [setting] out reasons why getting better is about people, not about politics, professional posturing and pride. Well or ill, we're in it, together." (Petit-Zeman, 2005)

In a similar vein, David Whyte (Whyte,1994) talks about 'inviting the soul to work'. He says that the soul has been relegated to the home and the church, not work ('the broken bridge'). This is regrettable, he says, since the soul is the centre of a person's creative application to work, and the source of energy in whatever he or she does. If work is all about doing, the soul is all about being; if work is our world, our soul is our home. The issue is one of melding soul life with work life; the inner ocean of longing and belonging, with the outer world of strategy and organisational control – two opposing sides of ourselves, normally split by the pressures of work.

A number of people in health policy and health improvement have commented on what they also perceive as this need for new strategies, for example Helen Bevan and Paul Plsek (Bate, Robert and Bevan, 2004):

"The NHS Plan cannot be delivered unless staff start breaking all the rules. We need a second order approach to change - getting rid of the old rule book and experimenting with new ways of doing things, redesigning the whole system."

These thoughts were echoed by Don Berwick, CEO of the Institute for Healthcare Improvement in Boston, USA (Berwick, 2003):

> "At present, prevailing strategies [in healthcare] rely largely on outmoded theories of control and standardisation of work. More modern, and much more effective theories seek to harness the imagination and participation of the workforce in reinventing the system."

Much current leadership practice is based on models for changing people's behavious which are highly questionable. Evidence from both workplace observation and clinical studies demonstrates that change efforts based on 'carrots and sticks' (incentives and threats) rarely work in the long-term (Rock and Schwartz, 2009).

Reinforcing this point of view, a recent study by McKinsey and Company (Leslie, Loch, Schaninger, 2006) considered the relationship between management incentives and performance in 230 businesses around the world, and collected data from more than 115,000 individual managers and employees.

1. STARTING FROM A DIFFERENCE PLACE

Figure 4 summarises the 'less effective' and 'more effective' practices for incentivising performance as revealed by the study:

Less effective	More effective
• Simplistic solutions	• An environment that encourages openness and trust, and challenge
• Internal competition	
	• Broad, stretching aspirations that are meaningful to staff
• Process driven efficiency	
	• Clear roles and accountabilities combination of complementary practices
• Standardisation and consistency	
• Sticks and carrots of incentives	
	• Starting from the organisational legacy and what people are used to
• Key Performance Indicators and other controlled mechanism applied in isolation	
• Dominant and/or detailed top-down leadership	
• Detailed strategies and plans	

Figure 4:
Source: *Leslie, Loch, Schaninger (2006) 'Managing your organisation by the evidence'*

Interestingly, three practices for incentivising performance were common among many of their high-performing organisations. These complementary and synergistic practices were:

• clarifying roles and accountabilities
• articulating a compelling direction and vision for the future, and
• developing a strong performance-oriented culture based on openness and trust.

But, despite the wide recognition that new strategies are needed, healthcare has largely continued to employ traditional approaches to change and performance improvement.

▶ 1.3 What do real-life case studies tell us about alternative approaches?

Despite centrally-driven models of change being predominant in healthcare, there are, nonetheless, inspiring stories of people working together in the NHS to achieve significant and lasting change. These are typically people who have broken out of the mould and refused to do it at the usual pace or in the usual way. As a result, they have achieved things that even they never believed possible.

One example is the story of David Shiers and the 'Early Psychosis Declaration'.

Case study: David Shier's story

These are David's own words (as cited in Bate and Robert, 2007):

"I had a General Practice; my wife's a district nurse and we just sailed into it looking for a good life really. We decided it was a good job, really nice place to work; it was good, it was easy. We got all sorted out, middle-class and it was all going very well and then something happens. So my daughter became difficult and I thought that was about the worst adolescence I'd seen. I'd been going to lots of families as a GP, quite dysfunctional families and in our own family things seemed far worse; I couldn't understand why. That was odd and then she started to see faces at the window and stuff and we began to realise that things weren't right and then she tried to kill herself. She put some paper into a socket; she brought us upstairs to see her do it and we suddenly thought, 'God, this is something serious'.

At that point we sort of panicked, probably appropriately. So we called in for help. A psychiatrist comes in from a children's service and says my daughter's got schizophrenia. And we were surprised because my wife had done psychiatric nursing and hadn't seen it. We thought she was depressed and was being bullied.

"Kids' toys ... you know for a 16-year-old and the toys are Teletubbies or something and you're sat there thinking you're not in the right place and it was grotty"

So essentially we had a two-weekly appearance at a grotty little children's outpatients. Kids' toys ... you know for a 16-year-old and the toys are Teletubbies or something and you're sat there thinking you're not in the right place and it was grotty. And the psychiatrist, God bless him, used to say, 'There's nothing we can offer here'. I think his words were – 'if you just hang on to the adult service then we're into psychosis', and for 12 months you had nothing more than that.

So eventually there was a bank holiday weekend, Mothering Sunday actually, and I was on call. It was my thirtieth phone call and my daughter was convinced that every phone call was about her and we just couldn't contain it; she became very angry, very distressed, running around the house.

We had 12 months and that was it really. She had a paranoia extended to not just me, because that was one of the difficulties - very, very paranoid towards me. But when that paranoia extended to mum and grandma, who's a key figure, that's it, it just fell apart. So within 48 hours she found herself in an acute adult ward, at just 17, into the most chaotic environment you could ever believe. It was bedlam really. And for 48 hours of that we thought it was the first time we'd ever had a break really for 12 months. My wife had given up her job. I was lucky to go out to work. So we thought, 48 hours, wow – we can just relax.

And there's two other kids in this family and then we realised that first of all my daughter's illness was getting worse in this environment – it was such a punitive and inappropriate environment really – and she spent six months in an acute adult ward because there was nowhere else for a 17-year-old with a psychosis to go. I was told it was that rare, but you know, it was not that rare. Everyone told us it would get slightly better, but it all seemed to get worse and when anyone made a prediction, it didn't improve, it got worse. So we realised that we were in a service that didn't deal with young people. We'd gone from a children's service that didn't do psychosis to an adult centre that didn't do young people. It was daft. I couldn't have dreamt of designing a service that was more inappropriate for teenage onset of this psychosis, this 15 to 25-ish age group.

"This rehab was a lie – it wasn't rehab at all really; it was just a warehouse, eight-bedded dormitory, no carpets, no curtains - 17 ½ years old, going nowhere really. It was always getting worse"

So six months there. Eventually it was suggested that she go into a rehab setting and that was in the old 'bin' where I was a GP and practised there. And there was this asylum and I used to drive past it and used to be GP to quite a few of the staff and I never understood it really. And then I did understand it. This rehab was a lie – it wasn't rehab at all really; it was just a warehouse, eight-bedded dormitory, no carpets, no curtains - 17 ½ years old, going nowhere really. It was always getting worse.

Then there was a transformative incident – Jane. Jane arrived as a new psychiatrist and within three or four days of her being in post, literally within days, she called my wife and I to her office and said she thinks she'll complain. So that was a transformational moment. And Jane explained that there wasn't things – like there wasn't an OT [occupational therapist], there wasn't a psychologist.

"I couldn't see any future. I just craved for the boys to leave home and find a future and my wife and I would just be doomed – this is your path"

She said she would deal with that but she's just a psychiatrist and she was being quite blunt about what the service didn't have. And she also said that my daughter had got a very bad illness and they would do their best, but you know ... I think the real basis of that point was, how can this be right for a 16 1/2 – 17-year-old, putting her into a bin with no possible hope – it is totally hopeless..

There was never going to be anything of a life, she was just blighted really and that's how it would be. And her future was mapped out – she was going to stay in an institution for the rest of her days and our shoulders would be down as a family. It felt very, very grey – not so much angry as very grey. I couldn't see any future. I just craved for the boys to leave home and find a future and my wife and I would just be doomed this is your path. And I couldn't see any way out of it. So, in a sense, all we did was go from day to day. My wife and I used to talk at night when the kids were asleep and just say, well, that's another day.

Deep down, I think, I was very, very distressed."

▶ What happened next?

Faced with this scenario, David felt impelled to act to stop being a comfortable, private, middle-class GP and to move into the more treacherous seas of being an activist and joining with others in creating a movement for change.

Remarkably, David's story ends with 'The Early Psychosis Declaration' (EPD) (see figure 5). David and colleagues he subsequently met along the way played a key role in the development of the EPD.

The EPD is an International Consensus Statement about Early Intervention and Recovery for young people, jointly issued in May 2004 by the World Health Organisation (WHO) and the International Early Psychosis Association.

Why do we need the Early Psychosis Declaration

The World Health Organisation estimates that the burden of psychosis borne by a family was only succeeded by quadriplegia and dementia.

Personal Experiences say:

"…our overwhelming feeling was of an opportunity missed – to what degree she has been needlessly disabled by those first four years of care we will never know"

"services just seemed to passively wait until he was really ill – the service oozed pessimism, lack of investment and lack of imagination"

"…Can't get a job, can't get a girlfriend, can't get a telly, can't get nothing…It's just everything falls down into a big pit and you can't get out"

To view the declaration in full visit
www.rethink.org/earlypsychosisdeclaration

Figure 5: *Extracts from the Early Psychosis Declaration*

The Declaration sets out five key objectives for action to provide much-needed support for young people who develop psychosis. This helps young people to access quality mental health services and social intervention initiatives at the early stages of their illness, making a lasting difference to the lives of young people with psychosis, their families and carers. In summing up Dr. Benedetto Saraceno, Director of Mental Health at WHO, said:

> "We need committed people, we need good will people, we need grass-roots people, because as indicated in the suggested actions of the Declaration, this is a task for us all, each one with their possibilities and capabilities, but all together, and first of all with service users."

In a large part it was the example of David's story that led us to the phrase, 'the power of one, the power of many', and it echoes American cultural anthropologist Margaret Mead's advice to.

> "Never doubt that a small group of thoughtful committed citizens can change the world. Indeed it is the only thing that ever has."

Such examples and insights suggest that every one of us has the potential to be an activist, even, if like David, initially a reluctant activist. Clearly he and the others he worked with had a personal cause that came from deep within. Indeed, many such 'David' stories have broadly the same elements and many of these will apply to any individual who chooses to go down a similar route. (See figure 6.)

- vested interest
- anger
- personal
- passion - collective
- crossing formal boundaries
- connections
- core values
- recognition by external person that anger = energy
- anger was controlled and not unbridled
- time and place   people coming together and lining up
- anyone can become an activist = mostly because there is an imperative
- grievance combined with commitment
- courage

Figure 6: *Characteristics observed in David Shiers' case study*

Experiences of families like David's constitute a social injustice and while 10 years ago David describes how 'as a family we felt written-off', today he truly believes they are now beyond the crossroads on their journey.

2. A NEW WAY OF THINKING

There are any number of remarkable stories like David's, and others are included in this publication can be found in the appendices. Studying these stories reveals a number of recurring themes:

- a deep sense of commitment and connection between the individuals involved and the cause they are fighting for (often that commitment will sit alongside a genuine sense of grievance)
- they have tremendous energy and generate energy in the people around them, and
- they do not achieve their goals alone; they bring other people on board with them.

2.1 Social movements

Drawing on these themes, the NHS Institute for Innovation and Improvement has been looking at where the NHS can find new paradigms of change that are characterised by the same commitment, passion, energy, mass, and momentum. Our search – as described in Bate and Robert (forthcoming) – led us to **social movement thinking**.

We need to start by understanding what we mean by social movements.
A social movement can be defined as:

> A voluntary collective of individuals committed to promoting or resisting change through co-ordinated activity.

Social movements produce a lasting and self-generating effect, and create, as they do this, a sense of shared identity.

Commonly cited social movements include: labour movements (Solidarity), religious movements, environmental movements (Greenpeace), and civil rights movements (suffragettes). Some movements consist of little more than a 'cultural drift' – a discernable yet decentred and unorganised shift in particular ways of thinking, acting and perceiving. Drifts are 'movements' but they entail no protest. Movements can in fact do much more besides protesting.

In the context of healthcare improvement, we are concerned with social movements as enduring collective action rather than passing forms of collective behaviour (such as panics, riots, fads and fashions).

'Collective action' in this sense refers to a broad range of purposeful collective behaviour, the most organised of which are social movements that occur over longer time stretches; are driven by long-term goals; and develop into formal organisations.

Figure 7: *Some social movements that may be familiar*

One in particular that captures the sense of what is possible when individuals come together is this quotation from Lech Wałęsa of the Polish Solidarity movement seen here:

"Each of us individually does not count much. But together we are the strength of millions who constitute Solidarity"

Lech Wałesa

Figure 8

▶ 2.2 Core features of social movements

A review of the social movements literature (Bate, Bevan and Robert, 2004) suggests eight core features of social movements:

1. Public protest and the use of *radical and unconventional* means of political persuasion is a fundamental feature of most movements, large and small – their purpose being either to foster or to halt change. This is based on the belief that change cannot be achieved within the system and so aspects of the system itself have to be changed.

2. Social movements can be transformative events; writers have argued that all major changes in the US have been brought about as the result of a social movement; never a planned – and certainly not an incremental – programme of change.

3. Collectivity and commonality define a movement; the whole basis of a movement being joint action, common outlooks, shared goals and collaboration.

4. People do not have to join a social movement; they join because of choice and some kind of commitment to join with others. 'Movements' are voluntary, not a 'programme' as such: they are spontaneous and self-organising.

5. Social movements are wonderful examples of organisation and disorganisation. They explode into life without being organised, but if they are to stay in existence they need central co-ordination and resourcing.

6. Movements are contentious and movement participants are usually 'protesters' or 'heretics' of one kind or another.

7. Movements relate to the 'underlife' of an organisation or society, often seeking to avoid detection. They are also often seen as an unwelcome, subversive or forbidden oppositionary force.

8. Social movements are not fly-by-night phenomena that are here today and gone tomorrow. The kind of changes movements pursue, whatever their size, typically require some measure of *sustained, organised activity.*

In turn, these core features manifest themselves in seven common characteristics of social movements (Bate, Bevan and Robert, 2004):

• Energy
• Mass
• Passion
• Commitment
• Pace and Momentum
• Spread
• Longevity

These are characteristics that are sometimes glimpsed in the NHS - witnessed in the story of David Shiers - but which are so often not embedded in the day-to-day experience of staff and patients. The challenge is to bring these features to bear in the way we go about making improvement happen in the NHS.

▶ 2.3 Social movements and scale

Importantly in the context of system-wide healthcare improvement efforts, social movements also involve scale. For example, the environmental movement – 'The most comprehensive and influential movement of our time' (Castells, 1997) comprises in the US alone over 10,000 environmental organisations, with a combined membership of over 41 million (Brulle, 2000).

In 2000, a national survey in Britain found that 20% of respondents belonged to some kind of environmental organisation (Johnson and Jowell, 2001). The aggregated membership of national environmental movement organisations in Britain exceeded 5 million by the late 1990s (ibid). In the Netherlands the proportion is even higher: in 2001 this figure was 3.7 million in a country with a population of 16 million. And the achievements of the environmental movement are many:

> *"There have been many great battles, and many defeats, but it is hard to imagine that so much of the Californian redwood forests or the Alaskan wilderness, the Great Barrier Reef, the Australian wet tropics or the Tasmanian forests would have been saved without the efforts of environmentalists."* (Johnson and Jowell, 2001)

Social movement research has become a major field of research today, especially in the US (see reference section for various books, journals and recent conferences). It is therefore time to think seriously about what it may have to offer to organisational change in healthcare, especially in the light of some of the inconsistent results from organisational development and planned change efforts to-date.

Social movement and organisation theorists alike have recognised that change is usually gradual and evolutionary; often running out of steam before reaching its final destination. The question is how to speed it up and give it the energy it needs to ensure the desired results are reached.

▶ 2.4 Social movements and NHS improvement

With this in mind, we have often asked NHS staff to share an experience they have had of joining together with others to achieve something at home or at work.

- How did it feel?
- What made them join?
- What are the features/characteristics of the movement?
- What factors enabled it to form?
- Why do they think people join?

The intriguing follow-up question and challenge is: can these dynamics be created within healthcare organisations to drive wider, deeper, faster change and service improvement? Or are organisations different?

We have asked what would it look like if these characteristics could be embedded in the day-to-day work of the NHS; how would the new approach need to differ from the current ones? This exercise demonstrates that people intuitively recognise that a movement approach would generate a different level of engagement and participation from traditional models of change management (see figure 9).

How would work to eradicate healthcare acquired infections be different if it were a movement?

Current approach	Movement approach
• Inconsistent implementation • Dissipated • Top-down • Not core • Observe from the top • Reactive, crisis • Stop/start • In silos	• Passion, energising • Everybody's business • Input from staff • Proactive • Preventative • Spread throughout health community • Multi-disciplinary • Constant, gathering pace • Personal responsibility (are you passing the bug on?) • Practical, eg patient focus

Figure 9: *NHS workshop participants' view on how a national priority would be affected by a movement approach*

These views are consistent with comparisons we have drawn between social movement thinking and current organisational thinking around change. In drawing these comparisons, we do not seek to discredit existing approaches. Rather we think it is important to articulate what social movements thinking can offer that is different.

Programatic approach	Movement approach
• a planned programme of change with central goals and milestones (centrally led)	• change is about releasing energy – largely self-directing and bottom-up
• talks about 'motivating' people'	• talks about 'moving people'
• change is driven by the appeal to 'what's in it for me'	• there may be personal costs involved
• talks about 'overcoming resistance'	• insists that change needs opposition – it is the friend not the enemy of change
• change is done 'to' people or 'with' them – leaders and followers	• people change themselves and each other – peer-to-peer
• driven by formal systems	• driven by informal social networks

Figure 10: *How is a movements approach different from a traditional programmatic approach?*
Adapted from Bate, Bevan and Robert, 2004.

2. A NEW WAY OF THINKING

Some of the key distinctions between the two approaches in figure 10 are that a programme approach typically looks at change as something that is centrally-led with goals, targets and milestones. In contrast, a movements approach thinks of change as the process of releasing energy around a cause (often quite vague and unfocused at first) and being largely self-directing and bottom-up. And while a programme approach talks about 'motivating people' as if just getting the incentives right will lead to people to do what is required, a movement approach talks about 'moving' people, tapping into their personal beliefs and will to make a change.

But the social movement perspective is not just a different way of **doing** things; it is also a different way of **thinking** about things, and a different way of **relating to** each other. Recent work at London Business School (Hamel, 2006) suggests that organisation leaders typically hold a set of widely-held views about change, which although they may contain some truth within them, are not the whole truth and have come to constrain the way change is approached and what is considered to be achievable.

So, how does a social movement view of change differ from the typical prevailing views that leaders hold about change? (Figure 11.)

Current prevailing beliefs about change	A movement perspective of change
• change starts at the top	• change builds from bottom-up action
• it takes a crisis to provoke change	• change can be driven by passion to improve
• only a strong leader can change a large institution	• change comes from collective action of individuals
• to lead change you need a clear agenda	• you need to have a clear cause but can be uncertain about how you will achieve it
• most people are against change	
• change management is a disciplined process	• people have an inner desire to make things better
	• change is opportunistic and spontaneous

Figure 11: *How does a movement view of change differ from our current view?*
Source: NHS Institute, 2008

From a movements perspective, there is clearly a different approach to change that challenges the fundamental assumptions of current beliefs and presents new possibilities.

Finally, another contrast is between the 'logic' that drives the way organisations function and the 'consciousness' that guides movements (figure 12). The rules and regulations that characterise the logic of authority often serve to hinder rather than help change:

> "The problem is not lazy or incompetent people; it is red tape and regulation so suffocating that they stifle every ounce of creativity ... the federal government is filled with good people trapped in bad systems... faced with so many controls, many employees have simply given up. They do everything by the book - whether it makes sense or not." (Gore, 1993)

One example (cited by Kelman, 2005) is New York City's efforts to rebuild the ice rink in Central Park in the 1980s. After six years of effort and an expenditure of $13 million, the rink had still not been rebuilt. Then Donald Trump took charge, committing to having contractors he selected complete the job within six months at a price no greater than $3million. The job came in one month ahead of schedule and $750,000 under budget.

Similarly, consider what new possibilities could be created in healthcare improvement if:

- **action and decision-making were really devolved rather than centralised; where people could take action without reference back up the chain**

- **power was exercised by an empowered staff rather than just those with formal authority**

- **participation was voluntary and open rather than selective or coerced; people did what they wanted to do, not what someone else wanted them to do**

- **staff engaged with a 'cause' on an emotional level and gave their commitment and will, rather than just their compliance to a target**

2. A NEW WAY OF THINKING

Figure 12: *What is the difference between organisational logic and 'movement consciousness'?*

The logic of organisation/authority	The consciousness of mobilisation and social movements
• formal ties	• informal ties
• hierarchical	• equal and fraternal
• bureaucratic	• communal and consensus-based
• centralised	• devolved
• led from the top (the privilege of the powerful)	• participative and led from the bottom (the privilege of the less powerful)
• coercive	• voluntary
• legitimate authority	• empowered
• rational	• emotional
• planning/order	• action/emergence

Source: NHS Institute, 2008

In summary, we are seeking to articulate an additional approach to change. It is about having a greater choice of strategies to draw on and adding on some of the critical things that are missing from current change efforts. As Palmer (1977) suggests:

> *"The genius of social movements is paradoxical: they abandon the logic of organisations so that they can gather the momentum necessary to alter the logic of organisations."*

Another way of thinking about this is through the idea of right brain/left brain approaches to change. Our current approaches in the NHS are predominantly 'left brain thinking' – ie the 'clinical systems' metaphor of improvement (see figure 13).

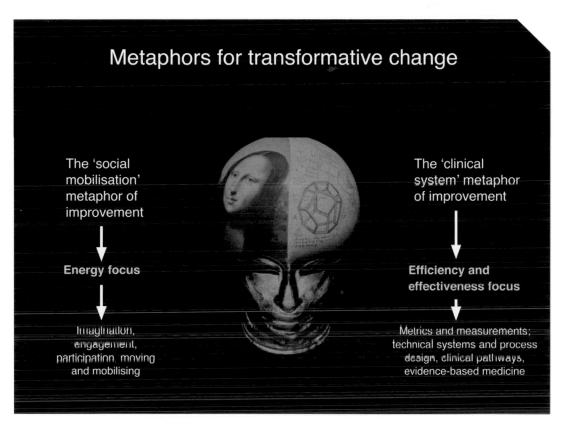

Figure 13: *Right brain/left brain approaches to change*
Adapted from Bate, Mendel and Robert, 2008

Gareth Morgan (Morgan, 1996) says:

> *"One of the most basic problems of modern management is that the mechanical way of thinking is so ingrained in our everyday conception of organisations that it is often difficult to organise in any other way."*

To take the clinical systems metaphor to its extreme, we think in terms of 'inputs and outputs', maximising 'production' and making 'efficiency the driving force'. When things are going well we say the organisation is running like clockwork; a 'well-oiled engine' or an 'assembly line'. When they are not, then communication has 'broken down'. In response we want to get down to the 'nuts and bolts' of the operation. We conduct 'time and motion' studies and attempt to quantify and measure everything.

Furthermore, often when attempting to bring in 'right brain' thinking, it is applied through a left brain perspective, eg let us have a project plan for engaging with staff. Many of the focal points on the right-hand side are about social relationships as opposed to task relationships – hence it is not about trying to create an organisational as opposed to social movement, but a social movement within an organisational context.

What if we adopted a 'social mobilisation' metaphor of improvement as well; a focus on energy and energising people, built around imagination, engagement, participation, moving and mobilising? Large-scale change efforts within the NHS are much more likely to falter because we fail to adopt a 'social mobilisation' perspective, than because we fail in our efficiency and effectiveness focus (NHS Institute, 2009).

Ultimately, our challenge is to be able to hold both these approaches in mind at once, while recognising that there are going to be tensions and difficult encounters between them. The problem is that in an organisation context, we cannot take these constraints away, but have to find ways of working with and around them; always resisting the normative pull to come back 'into line' in what we think and do.

> "The way past this is to cultivate ambivalence and a degree of schizophrenia - best summed up as acting as though the organisation does not exist, but knowing that it does"

The way past this is to cultivate ambivalence and a degree of schizophrenia - best summed up as 'acting as though the organisation does not exist, but knowing that it does'. Despite this, the strength of the prevailing left brain thinking will mean that there will be a strong tendency to revert to it. So the challenge is to try to embed an additional perspective on change that can be applied in local contexts – exactly what we have been testing.

3. THE CASE FOR SOCIAL MOVEMENT THINKING

At this point the reader may well be asking 'why should I believe any of this? And anyway, are social movements not completely different from organisations?'

Both are reasonable questions. In response, it is important to point out that these ideas are based on a combination of academic research, sound evidence and the testament of practitioners who have been trying out these ideas within real NHS organisations.

The principles that we have distilled from social movement thinking for NHS improvement are a distillation of a huge evidence base around social movements (some of it about real-life healthcare and organisational movements) which recently has begun to argue that it is possible to create movement-like processes in organisations (David and Zald, 2005).

There has been a determined effort to make the approach 'evidence-based' - unlike most change and improvement work which is often intuitive and not connected to the literature or research.

In addition, we have worked with a small number of NHS pilot sites who volunteered to try out some of the ideas over a six-month period to see whether there was an initial 'proof of concept' and whether it was worth moving on to the next stage. The types of local issues the test sites tackled included: major service reconfiguration; improved pathways; healthcare associated infections; business planning; changes to clinical practice; ward improvements; and improved patient experience.

The outcomes of this, although still early days, have been promising. We have learnt a tremendous amount and people have been very positive about the approach and what it has achieved. The following pages (38 - 46) contain just a small selection of comments from the field test sites.

IT IS DIFFERENT:

"I think there's certainly more freedom. I don't mean it's not organised but there's more opportunity to probably think outside of the box and be a bit different"

Calderdale & Huddersfield NHS Foundation Trust

"With some project deadlines you feel that they are put on you and forced, and I think this is trying to get around all that and being abou us wanting to bring about the change ourselves"

Calderdale & Huddersfield NHS Foundation Trust

"And so I think it is very different in the sense that it puts a lot more emphasis on the absolutely key things. I think that the principles really are the key things, and it really, really brings them to the surface, and you can really see and understand the power of those things, and pick up really practical ideas on how to do it... So I think it is different. I'm converted. I think about it a lot"

Calderdale & Huddersfield NHS Foundation Trust

"If you actually sat in one of the meetings and felt the energy, the energy is unbelievable. It's as if you could sort of touch it, the enthusiasm. The energy and the enthusiasm"

Patients Council, North East Manchester Sector

"Well it went from a group that had never met before in January to them wanting to meet in the evenings once a week because they were so enthused about the whole thing. It was incredible how this happened"

North East Manchester Sector PCT

"And we really are seeing staff with the belief they can change things for the better and this 'we can do', attitude. And I think what's quite striking is when we first had the meetings and we had a lot of the reasons why we can't do this; we can't change that because of this system, we can't change that…
And we've started to see now in the meetings less of the reasons why they can't change things, and I think that's because they're now feeling, yes, we have the ability to make changes. And they are becoming more challenging of themselves and not seeking permission all the time."

Calderdale & Huddersfield NHS Foundation Trust

NHS
Institute for Innovation and Improvement

"And they've taken on personal responsibility as a set of individuals and a group to change the future for themselves"

Milton Keynes General Hospital

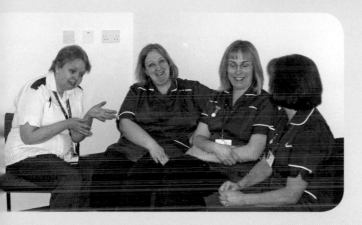

"And what you need to do is say to people, it's in your hands ... People feel that they're powerless. And what I think they don't realise is the power that they've got... I don't know, it might just be me, but I think the power is in my hands, personally, I take responsibility for things that I will accept or that I won't accept...And if you work from the bottom and dig your foundations, surely the building will rise above it."

Patients Council, North East Manchester Sector

BOTTOM-UP CHANGE:

"Well, I think the clinical side was a movement in itself where we had five PEC chairs who had never met in January and were given a task to deliver the clinical proposals and, by May, had 500 health clinics, healthcare professionals, or a mixture of 100 consultants plus a load of GPs and nurses and everybody else, all working to redesign the services. And that went from nothing to a real swell of it...
And for this consultation it wasn't the Chief Executives saying, well, this service should be there and that should be there. It was the clinicians who told the Chief Executives what the reconfiguration would look like, which was a real bottom-up approach"

North East Manchester Sector PCT

CREATIVE PROBLEM-SOLVING:

"What's really noticeable is they are not just looking for just the traditional way of solving a problem anymore; they're really now starting to look at things much more differently and being more innovative, and this has come from a team who had no communication, were not good with the patients"

Calderdale & Huddersfield NHS Foundation Trust

PARTNERSHIP WORKING:

"But you've only got to sit round the table at the transport meetings and it's awesome. It really is awesome. Because you've got all these varying transport bodies sitting round a table and they're actually all talking together and offering to each other. And the very nature of all the different transport systems we have here, getting them to talk to each other, never mind sit around a table, is a big deal. And I was sort of really swept away with that transport meeting that I sat on. I thought, wow, and when you realised who all these people were, and they were all sharing ideas..."

Patients Council, North East Manchester Sector

ENGAGEMENT:

"it has created pockets of enthusiasm that are now affecting other areas... paediatrics have heard and seen what's going on with maternity and want to do the same which I think is good news"

Milton Keynes General Hospital

"But our strength's with the clinicians, and that's when we'll come into our own, because we had a great relationship with the clinicians... They loved what we do, they speak the same language, and therefore I think when that comes back into play, when you've got management, clinicians and us, then it will happen"

North East Manchester Sector PCT

"It is about working together across five teams in a way that they've never done before."

TANGIBLE OUTCOMES:

"We were tasked with clinicians designing the consultation, designed what we wanted to reconfigure and we've delivered that. We delivered the movement, delivered the proposals, which was consulted on by over 100,000 people so, in some respects, that has been a success. And our task was to do that and we've delivered that. We did deliver a genuine clinically led patient influenced consultation. That was our remit"

Issues Tackled:
- major service reconfiguration
- Improved pathways
- MRSA
- business planning
- changes to clinical practice
- ward improvements
- improved patient experience

3. THE CASE FOR SOCIAL MOVEMENT THINKING

▶ 3.2 The perceived benefits and risks: a polarity map exercise

What has been the wider reaction to the idea of bringing a social movement perspective to bear on NHS improvement efforts when we have shared it with other NHS improvement leaders?

We have used polarity mapping (Johnson, 1992) in workshops with NHS improvement leaders to explore the positive and negative aspects of both the traditional programmatic approach and a movements approach.

Polarity mapping is based on the premise that rather than looking for problems to solve, we should be seeking polarities to manage. This is a very helpful framework for thinking about a planned/programmatic approach versus a social movement approach because it helps show that rather than being either/or alternatives, they are different 'poles'. Going too far down one pole means we need to take actions to bring the situation back into equilibrium.

Figure 14 gives a typical example of the type of responses to the polarity mapping exercise. Readers are already likely to be very familiar with the strengths (top-left quadrant) and weaknesses (bottom-left quadrant) of the traditional approach. But reactions to the social movement perspective provide further testament from NHS practitioners that, though cautious of the potential downsides, there is 'something in this' idea (top-right quadrant).

Ideal future: large scale, sustainable Improvement for patients

Executive sign-up
Organised
Clear expectations and goals
What is in it for me?
Planning and order to give you a sanity check
Monitor progress, award appropriately
Person at top may be right (most experienced)
Underpin development
Building blocks
Measure/demonstrates improvement
Has credibility, tried and tested – gets results
Clear boundaries, clear aims
Traditional management sign-up

Lets people shine
Allows creativity
Freedom to innovate
Emergent strategy
Sustainable and more commitment
Allows champions - no rules
Peer-to-peer
Empowering
Bottom-up approach and bottom-up action
Starts from ground up for impetus plus
Ideas
Has its own momentum
Emotive
Mass – by using friends and connections
Mobilisation – continuous

Planned programatic approach to change

Movement approach to change

Not sustainable
Predictable and familiar
Those that shout loudest get heard
Process orientated -v- system understanding
Too prescriptive
Less flexible can leave people behind
Lack of common sense - too rigid
Bureaucratic forms, correct forum
Lacks sustainability – target achieved without hearts and minds
Hierarchical/restrictive/crisis-driven
Not empowering
Does not engage shop floor
Wasteful and expensive

Crisis provoking change
Too informal
Could be overcome by cynicism
Reliant on key individuals
Long timeline, not holistic
Less control
Could be chaotic
Opportunistic change
No end point
Loss of direction – duplication – fragmentation
Driven by informal social networks
To have consensus
Risk for individuals and organisation
Personal cost for staff with low morale
Sounds like more pressure
Bad ideas by loud/active group – pressure to agree
Relies on a person/crisis/ideas
Lack of responsibility
High-risk

Fears: Unable to deliver changes for patients

Figure 14: *'Polarity map' constructed in NHS workshops*

3.3 Making it happen in an organisation: five key principles

Over the past 24 months, the NHS Institute has been asking: can such social movement dynamics be created within an organisation? Drawing on the learning from our work with the field test sites; the experiences of other NHS organisations who have adopted these principles; and the literature around social movements, we have distilled the evidence-base and created a set of principles that we believe, if applied, can begin to create just these types of dynamics.

The five principles are:

1. change as a personal mission
2. frame to connect with hearts and minds
3. energise and mobilise
4. organise for impact
5. keep forward momentum.

One point to emphasise is that these principles are not a linear process. Rather they are inter-related and need to be considered together (see figure 15) if the features that characterise social movements are to begin to show in healthcare improvement efforts. Bearing this important point in mind, the principles suggest that individuals need to see change as a personal mission, for without the 'one' it is impossible to build the 'many'. It has to be 'my cause' something that 'I passionately believe in and want to do'.

Figure 15: *The inter-relation between the five principles*

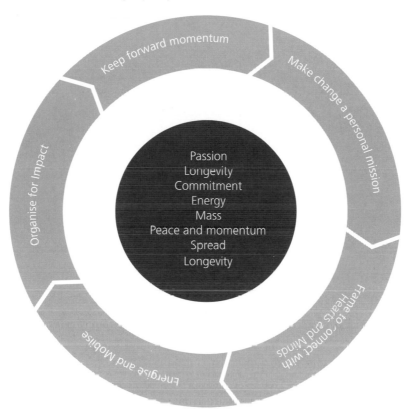

In seeking to apply these five principles to our improvement efforts, we need:

- to think about ourselves and the roles we play in a very different way; especially with regard to the way we make change happen
- to have a real 'cause' or ambition that we are passionate about and are willing to join with others to achieve
- a 'story' we can tell that will energise and mobilise others around our cause
- a well-thought-out set of methods, tactics and logistics
- a willingness to help construct and be part of a genuine social community in the workplace
- to bring the fun and soul back into improvement and welcome the chance to think in a totally different way.

Sections 4-8 explore just how we might achieve this.

4. CHANGE AS A PERSONAL MISSION

Later in this document we will discuss the need to develop and implement strategies and tactics to build mass and energy around healthcare improvement efforts. But we want to start by focusing on the single crucial factor that enables any cause or movement to succeed – the individuals who together make up a movement and whether each of them sees change as a personal mission.

Most movements are associated with key figurehead leaders but - as we shall come on to discuss in the 'organise for impact' principle - social movements are built on distributed leadership. While the role of a charismatic figurehead can help many movements, more important than a small number of individuals are the mass of people who bring the appropriate qualities and tactics to the cause.

4. 1 Characteristics of movements activists

An energised individual is an activist, and activists join with others to create campaigns and movements. To deliver significant change in the NHS, many of these same individuals will need to become 'organisational radicals' – activists who are not satisfied with the status quo in their healthcare organisation and willing to take some personal risk to achieve their goals.

A key characteristic of an organisational radical is that they work with their organisation to help improve it, rather than work against it. Of course, there are lots of different types of activists (see figure 16) but studies of movements show that there are a number of personal qualities that are often shared by these individuals.

Figure 16: *Types of movements activists*

- protestors (Greenham Common, Michael Collins)
- campaigners (Berwick, Steinham, Nadar)
- revolutionaries (Guy Fawkes, Ghandi, El Cid)
- community/social activists (Alinsky, Mandela)
- heretics (Kleiner, Luther, Copernicus)
- rebels (Spartacus, James Dean)
- dissenters and dissidents (Solzhenitsyn, Aung San Suu Kyi)
- educators (Freire, Palmer)
- reformists (Pankhurst, Martin Luther King, Washington, Elizabeth Fry)
- radical business thinkers (Peters, Senge, Handy)

Firstly courage is essential; being prepared to 'stick your neck out'. Courage can take a number of forms: the quiet courage of someone like Rosa Parks who sparked the civil rights campaign by sitting on the bus seats reserved for white people (figure 17), or the lone protestor who famously stood in the way of the tanks in Tiananmen Square (figure 18):

Figure 17: *Rosa Parks*

4. CHANGE AS A PERSONAL MISSION

Figure 18: *Tiananmen protestor*

Intriguingly, Parks was no victim; she had a long history of anti-racist activism. Indeed, she had often been expelled from the local buses for refusing to comply with the 'for whites only' directive (including 12 years previously by the same bus driver who lit the blue touch paper of the civil rights movement on that momentous day in 1955). Far from being a meek lady, she was a keen supporter of Malcolm X. Kohl writes that: "to call Rosa Parks a poor, tired seamstress, and not talk about her role as a community leader and civil rights activist as well, is to turn an organised struggle for freedom into a personal act of frustration".

These insights provide some important clues (which we shall return to) as to how social movement theory might begin to be applied in a healthcare context. They also highlight the need for courage - "courage is doing what you're afraid to do. There can be no courage unless you're scared" (Eddie Rickenbacker).

But what does courage look like in the NHS? Perhaps Steve Bolsin embodies that; someone who was prepared to pay a personal cost to challenge the professional arrogance of his fellow consultants.

> "But what does courage look like in the NHS? Perhaps Steve Bolsin embodies that; someone who was prepared to pay a personal cost to challenge the professional arrogance of his fellow consultants"

Dr Bolsin is the clinician widely credited with blowing the whistle when between 30 and 35 children underwent heart surgery at the Bristol Royal Infirmary between 1991 and 1995 and died unnecessarily as a result of sub-standard care. He claims he was virtually driven out of medicine in this country after proving to be the catalyst for the ensuing scandal.

Dr Bolsin's own words sum it up: *"In the end I just couldn't go on putting those children to sleep, with their parents present in the anaesthetic room, knowing that it was almost certain to be the last time they would see their sons or daughters alive."*

The second characteristic we see time and again is the energy, passion and, particularly, impatience that comes with wanting to change some aspect of the world. We see in it the actions of people like Bob Geldof - who famously said: 'Just give us your f****** money' at Live Aid - or Jamie Oliver whose indignation at the food we feed our children led to sweeping changes in schools (see 'energise and mobilise' principle later in this report).

In the healthcare improvement context Don Berwick of the Institute for Healthcare Improvement (US) typifies these characteristics.

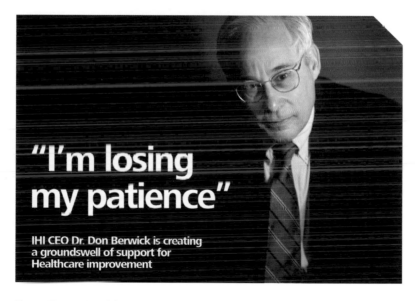

Figure 19: *Don Berwick*

Activists also combine a paradoxical combination of self-belief and self-doubt; it is this combination that brings with it the humility and determination with which people connect.

Persistence and stamina are other characteristics necessary for activists. Take Neville and Doreen Lawrence who campaigned for so long to gain justice for their son who was murdered by racists and in doing so re-defined our understanding of racism.

Finally, an important characteristic for activists is chutzpah or audacity; the sheer nerve that is required to take bold action and the ability to carry it off with confidence and panache.
This quote comes from a movement called the Industrial Areas Foundation which is a 'living wage, housing' movement in the US:

> "We do it with chutzpah. We don't let others set boundaries, barriers and distractions that prevent us from identifying the source of a problem and the shape of a solution. We don't see ourselves as squatters in the public square, but as full owners of what happens there."

▶ 4.2 From movement activists to organisational radicals

The objection to applying a social movements perspective to change in an organisational context is usually that change in societies (or any social system) is different from that in an organisation. However, there are some strong similarities in terms of the mechanisms by which organisations and social movements develop and change. Given these similarities, perhaps healthcare improvement efforts actually need more activists/radicals and many more radical ideas and practices?

Shifting the emphasis from movement activists to 'organisational radicals' also brings a specific set of characteristics to mind. There is a growing body of evidence that such organisational radicals share some characteristics with movement activists and are equally effective as agents of change. Typically, successful organisational radicals are:

- conviction-driven and values-driven, with a strong sense of self- belief that they are personally able to create change

- able to join forces with others and work as a collective body for commonly-valued changes (by igniting collective action, mobilising others, inspiring change)

- able to achieve small wins which precipitate a sense of hope and confidence

- optimistic in the face of challenge; see opportunities but take account of obstacles

- somehow 'different' from the traditional majority in their organisation

- a profound sense of purpose

- wanting to both rock the boat, and to stay in it; they walk the fine line between difference and fit, balancing conformity and rebellion; 'insider-outsiders', they work within systems not against them

- often 'everyday leaders' rather than chief executives, presidents or senior clinical leaders in organisations - yet they frequently have as critical a role in organisational change as the people with the formal authority (Meyerson, 2001)

Successful activists also need to understand the context in which they work. They need to be sensitive to the clinical, cultural, political and physical environment they are working within: who holds the power; what are the prevailing norms; what are the possibilities and limits? In the healthcare context this most likely means the clinical environment (pathways, processes); cultural environment (dominant cultural norms, values and ideas as revealed in events, stories, rituals, 'altars and sacred places'); political environment (tensions, conflicts, people who are 'in' and people who are 'out', where the power lies); physical and aesthetic environment; and constantly asking themselves how it looks and feels from both the staff and the patient points of view.

Successful activists are also able to 'schmooze the community' to build relationships, networks and alliances with those around them and to understand the main priorities and concerns (see 'organising for impact' principle later in this report).

4. CHANGE AS A PERSONAL MISSION

But what does being an 'improvement radical' or an 'improvement activist' in a healthcare organisational setting involve? How can individuals in an organisation act 'radically'? Healthcare improvement leaders might set out with radical ideas and hopes for the future, but they cannot ignore how organisations operate or what they have to do to fit in. Without 'quiet courage' they can often very quickly become normalised into the status quo of the organisation.

So when thinking of the role of leaders in healthcare improvement, and how difficult it is to get other people to change, there needs to be an understanding that the change process has to begin with individuals thinking differently about what they do. What are the assumptions that they make about how change happens? What are their theories around how to create change? These are the 'transformations in consciousness' that allow individuals to begin to look beyond the common sense, taken-for-granted ways of doing things. Without these transformations, individuals would simply reinforce the sense of normalisation by their own behaviour. Even though they might think that they are 'improvement activists' and radicals, many of their behaviours and actions may actually be reinforcing the status quo and not changing it. In short, change is also about a frame of mind. It grows out of the perspective that someone brings to the endeavour of implementing quality and service improvement. Change starts, therefore, with individuals.

An exercise we have run with a large number of NHS improvement leaders, to help them to begin to think about themselves as possible change activists, is to ask them to compile their 'Activist's CV':

- .What do you want to be remembered for?
- .What do you want your legacy to be?
- . What is the most inspiring thing you have ever done at work?
- . Who was affected by that?
- What did it mean to them?
- What do you do to walk the line between 'difference and fit' in your own context?
- When have you joined with others to take collective action?
- What do you contribute towards making the world a better place?
- What things keep you motivated and focused when the odds are stacked against you?
- What small wins have you accomplished that have led to bigger wins in the longer term?
- What are the other characteristics that make you a successful organisational radical?
- What personal insight have you gained from completing this CV?

Source: adapted from McConnel, 2003

Often those who complete the CV find that there is some aspect of their intrinsic motivation that they sometimes overlook; that they possess a shadow set of skills and values that they need to connect with more explicitly in order to be true to themselves and to have greater impact.

▶ 4.3 Risk and danger

A word of warning is warranted at this point; activists do need to manage risk and minimise danger.

> *"Modern heretics are not burned at the stake. They are relegated to backwaters or pressured to resign. They see their points of view ignored or their efforts undermined. They see others get credit for their ideas and work. Worst of all, they see the organisation thrive as a by-product of their efforts, while the point of their heresy, the truth they fought to bring to the surface, is lost."* (Kleiner, 1996)

Personal costs and personal risk are issues that will need to be considered by any activist and those involved in recruitment and mobilisation. And there is little doubt that the organisational context can be far more risky for the activist than the wider social arena. People are much less likely to join or participate in your movement when the risks of their doing so are high: "Whether individuals can be mobilised for risky forms of collective action with unclear pay-offs is highly problematic". (Strang and Jung, 2005: 308).

There are three major types of risk for organisational radicals (Meyerson, 2001). Firstly, they conform because they see no other choice and in doing so they surrender a part of themselves, silencing their commitment in order to survive. Secondly, they might leave the organisation because they cannot find a way to be true to their values and commitments and still survive. And thirdly, they stridently challenge the status quo in a manner which is increasingly radical and self-defeating - thus confirming what they already know that they do not belong.

Here are some views expressed by people involved in our field test sites that capture that sense of risk:

"If you're too successful people don't like it. I think it's that you become a threat. If you can deliver all this with one manager and an admin secretary, where are we all in this? ... It's almost like if your movement is too successful, people don't like it"

"The word risk, organisation risk, still comes harking back to it ... And I think the whole system creates a perpetuity around incremental improvement because, if you go for transformational and you get it wrong, then bye, bye. Who wants that?"

4. CHANGE AS A PERSONAL MISSION

So, how can organisational radicals survive? What tactics can they use? The key is to be able to rock the boat and stay in it. Meyersen calls such people 'tempered radicals'.

Definitions

Tempered
a) having the elements mixed in satisfying proportions; moderated
b) toughened by heating and cooling (like steel).

Radical
marked by a considerable departure from the usual or traditional.

Shepherd (Shepherd, 1975) developed some rules of thumb for activists to stay alive (and stay sane):

- stay alive
- start where the system is
- never work uphill
- do not build hills as you go
- work in the most promising area
- do not use one when two could do it
- do not over-organise
- do not argue if you cannot win
- play God a little
- innovation requires a good idea, initiative and a few friends
- load experiments for success
- light many fires
- keep an optimistic bias
- capture the moment.

Figure 20: *Shepherd's rules of thumb*
Source: Shepherd, 1975

As NHS leaders, we need to embrace our activists and radicals. Every new truth begins as herecy. As Kleiner (1996) says, corporate heretics may be the closest thing we have to genuine heroes. They are the unsung conscience of the NHS system (Bevan 2007b). As Hamel (2009) puts it, we need to "empower the renegades and disarm the reactionaries"

▶ 4.4 Defining your cause

All movements need a cause – the cause is what gives individuals the courage to act. So, a key question for any improvement activist in healthcare is: what is my cause?

> *"Often when people find a cause or something in the world that they believe in, they would do anything to make that happen. So that tapping into your courage is really related to tapping into your desire - what do you really want? What do you care about?"*
> (Whyte, 1994)

Building on the learning from our local NHS field-test sites, whenever we discuss this new approach with NHS improvement leaders, we ask them to think about a 'cause' that they wish to work on (contrasting this with a traditional project):. For instance, we will say:

> *"We will be asking you to work on your 'cause' - something you really care about. In preparation for this we would like you to go out and spend a day observing an area or activity that is likely to be affected by your cause and ask yourself, what is really going to make a difference here?"*

We often also pose the following scenario to improvement leaders when asking them to think about what their cause might be:

"Imagine if we could take any challenge – a specific service area improvement; no needless deaths; no MRSA; reducing inequalities; anything – and manage to:

* unleash energy
* mobilise a mass of people
* get pace and momentum behind the change
* arouse the passion in people's hearts
* get commitment 'to the cause' beyond the call of duty
* spread the change
* sustain it.

We then work with core teams of clinicians, nurses and managers that have come together as an 'activist community' to work on a shared cause that is meaningful to each of them (see the following case study).

CASE STUDY: Infection control in a NHS hospital system

A presentation about social movement thinking was made to a group of infection control link practitioners (the overall cause was 'infection prevention and control'). From this meeting, 14 staff put up their hand and said they were interested in getting involved in a social movement around this issue.

The initial idea was to get the individuals together to help them plan some work. In reality, the hospital was so busy this proved impossible. Instead, momentum was maintained by visiting the people individually. A series of questions were used to structure these meetings:

• What motivated you to become involved in reducing infection?

• What has happened since we last met?

• What contact/support have you had from your Infection Prevention and Control Nurse?

• What do you plan to do in your area to reduce infection?

• What did the presentation on social movement thinking mean for you?

• What do you want to change?

• Plans for time out/away day: what are your preferences?

The question: 'What do you want to change?' seemed to be the key one. It was this question that provoked the activists to talk about their own particular infection control passion. It was at this point that they themselves took the overall cause/frame and articulated their own particular 'mini' cause. Here are some examples:

Figure 21: *Examples of 'mini causes'*

Activist	Personal Cause	Their own framing
Staff nurse	Glove use	Gloves are not magic, they protect you from the patient but do not protect the patient from you! You still need to remove them and gel your hands
Staff nurse	Naked below the elbow	Clearly you cannot find anywhere to hang up your jacket ... here is a coat hanger!
Healthcare assistant	Naked below the elbow	If you are struggling to roll-up your sleeves I can help (wielding her scissors!)
Sister	Hand hygiene	Poster including template for picture of Hand Hygiene Champion - altered to include a mirror and the strap line Our Hand Hygiene Champion
Staff nurse	Unacceptable behaviours	Staff member refusing to remove jacket – challenged by staff nurse do you have kids? Then do you really want to take those bugs home to them?

It was these mini causes that the 'activists' were already using to engage and challenge colleagues. These personal frames were already working at the front line for people in their daily role, so it made sense to embrace and broadcast them. They were used in a further training session, both as examples of good framing, and to provide a selection of frames that these and other activists could use in their own workplace.

Mindful of movement-based tactics (ie campaigning and publicity) a series of articles was run in the hospital newsletter showcasing the 'activists' and highlighting the frames they had been using. This case study is, therefore, an example both of re-framing (see section 5) and of personalising a cause. The key for those leading the work locally was learning that although they had expected to have to sell the cause, the cause itself acted as a trigger which unlocked individual passions around infection prevention and control.

The most important point to highlight regarding the choice of 'cause' in an organisational setting is, therefore, that individuals need to be able to connect with it at a personal level; a movement-based approach to improvement simply will not work if the only motivation people have for doing something is that they are being paid to do it.

▶ 4.5 Causes as 'emotional buttons'

A cause is something that you passionately want to achieve and want to involve others in achieving. You are looking for 'emotional hot buttons' that will trigger the desired response (Gamson, 2004).

We know from the literature that effective causes typically do not threaten to displace other people's goals or causes, and strike a balance between narrow and broad focus. Too narrow a set of goals and you will not draw people to your cause. Too wide a set of goals and you will lose focus and spread your energy too thinly. We also know that people are more likely to join movements that seem likely to be successful (nobody backs a lost cause!). So people will also typically join when the opportunities and incentives for participation outweigh the costs (Taylor and Van Dyke, 2004). Recruiters, therefore, need to frame with this in mind.

So what makes a 'good' cause?

A good cause is:

- **not too broad, not too narrow**
- **worthy and worthwhile**
- **ambitious and lofty, yet achievable**
- **makes more friends than enemies (or isolates the enemies).**

5. FRAME TO CONNECT WITH HEARTS AND MINDS

Framing is generally seen to be the single most important principle of social movement thinking:

> "Social movement scholars have argued that in order to be successful, activists must frame issues in ways that resonate with the ideologies, identities, and cultural understandings of supporters and others who might be drawn to their cause ... [hence] framing has significant consequences for movement outcomes."
> (Campbell, 2005)

Our testing demonstrates that framing is also the most important concept in applying social movement thinking to healthcare improvement. It is through effective framing that movements make connections and mobilise people behind their cause. Snow and Benford (Snow and Benford, 1988) describe framing activities as:

> "The conscious, strategic efforts of movement groups to fashion meaningful account of themselves and the issues at hand in order to motivate and legitimise their efforts."

The test of a good frame is, therefore, the very practical one that people actually join in your cause - moving from bystanders, fence-sitters, free riders, or opponents, to supporters (Gamson, 2004). However, as McAdam suggests, at a minimum people need to feel both aggrieved about some aspects of their lives and optimistic that, by acting collectively, they can redress the problem. If one or both of these perceptions is lacking, it is highly unlikely that people will mobilise even when given the opportunity to do so.

Framing is, therefore, the key to turning opportunity into action.

"Our testing demonstrates that framing is the most important concept in applying social movement thinking to healthcare"

5. FRAME TO CONNECT WITH HEARTS AND MINDS

5.1 What do we mean by framing?

Frames

• are like picture frames: what is in it, you see, what is outside you do not. Successful movements are highly effective in drawing attention to the key themes and ideas behind their cause;

• provide shape and structure for organising ideas and arguments. They help lead people through complex issues to a shared conclusion;

• are 'hooks' for pulling people in; an effective frame will connect with people in a way that makes them pay attention. Frame something one way, and I get your attention and commitment; but frame it another way, and it goes right over your head;

• are 'springboards for mobilising support'. They can tap into the energy within people that even they may be surprised to find they have. The social movement literature talks about 'tapping in to sentiment pools' - those sources of boundless energy inside each of us; the energy that can pour out and get us moving even when we are totally exhausted.

Framing, therefore, has a number of important roles. It:

• draws people's attention to the movement
• articulates the cause, aims and solutions of the movement in compelling ways
• gives the cause legitimacy and worth ('rationales for action')
• recruits people and 'hooks' them in
• taps into the huge stores of potential energy that, for whatever reason, has not been released
• generates consensus
• influences and mobilises people into taking action (hence: "A successful framing strategy may increase...the movement's mobilisation potential by creating sympathy, support and goodwill that may convert into useful, practical resources of various sorts" (Gamson, 2004)
• shapes wider public thinking and discourse
• pre-empts or defeats antagonists' arguments and strategies.

Framing is fundamentally different from 'spin'. Framing relies on authenticity and a connection with an individual's reality. The images below demonstrate how an effective framing of an issue can change the way you view it, or make you think twice about your actions.

Figure 22: *Frames that make you think differently*

The evidence is very clear about some of the key elements of framing

5. FRAME TO CONNECT WITH HEARTS AND MINDS

▶ 5.2 The importance of credibility

We know from reviewing the literature that frames are more likely to be accepted if they are credible. This is absolutely critical: they need to be credible in terms of their resonance with current mainstream beliefs and experiences; they need to be credible in terms of the claims that they make; and they need to be delivered by credible individuals.

Frames also need to be salient; compatible with the life experiences of your audience.
An example of non-resonant 'bad' framing would be the 'Back to Basics' campaign which John Major ran when he was Prime Minister. Not only did it fail to resonate with the progressive society (salience), but it also lacked credibility because of what the public perceived to be contradictory 'sleaze' (failure to practice what you preach).

Typically, frames also work best when they are positive and optimistic (glass half-full rather than half-empty).

▶ 5.3 Some typical problems with framing

At the same time, it is worth reminding ourselves of some typical problems with framing:

a misalignment: the mismatch, or failure of correspondence, between proffered framing and target audience (eg, focusing on perpetrator or responsible agent to the neglect of victim, or vice versa)

b scope: when the scope of the frame is either too broad and over-extended or too narrow and restricted in terms of diagnosis or prognosis (eg, homeless movements target the federal government for local change)

c exhaustion: when frames become over-used and taken-for-granted; they become tired and spent (eg, the traditional racist framing that the 'New Racist White Separatist' (NRWS) movement tried to turn on its head)

d relevance: when a frame is out of touch with or contradicted by the flow of events (eg, predicament confronting anti-war movement in US after the war began).

▶ 5.4 Getting it right: approaches for effective framing

▶ 5.4.1 Hooking people in

So what are some of the key things you need to do to frame effectively?

In order to create the right dynamics for a social movement, you need to build mass. That means you need to be able to hook in a range of different stakeholders.

The first task is therefore to think about the different people you need in order achieve your goals. We tend to think about stakeholders in terms of their role or position in the system. A movement approach tends to think more in terms of their readiness to act: believers; sympathisers; ambivalents; antagonists; the disaffected; the people who have given up saying: 'it doesn't ever get better so why bother?'

It is essential to frame differently for each of these target groups, identifying ways of attracting them to your cause. In some cases it will even be necessary to segment them further into other relevant groupings, for instance, different frames for different professional roles. In short, improvement leaders adopting a movement approach need to attract their target groups to their cause by thinking themselves into their shoes.

Framing infection control

	Bad Frame?	Good frame?
Doctors	Halving MRSA rates is a Government Target	Focus on the basics of excellent clinical care (peer-to-peer)
Nurses	You must balance the need for beds with infection control	Patients' safety and dignity come first
Infection Control Staff	Changing staff behaviour is your responsibility	You have CEO/Board support to do what needs to be done to eradicate infections
The Board	It will be mandatory for a senior nurse to report rates at every Board meeting	Preventing avoidable infections tops the Boards' strategic objectives and supports the achievment of other objectives
The Public	Avoidable infections are caused by visitors and the public	Help us, help ypu

Figure 23: 'Bad' and 'good' framing for specific stakeholder groups
Source, Julie Wells, Luton and Dunstable NHS Foundation Trust, 2007

▶ 5.4.2 Connect with people's hearts ... and minds

The next key approach to effective framing is the need to connect with people's emotions - their hearts. As John Kotter (Kotter, 2002) suggests:

> "People change what they do less because they are given analysis that shifts their thinking than because they are shown a truth that influences their feelings."

As improvement leaders we need to define goals in a way that connects with people's intrinsic motivation and values. One example comes from the earlier case study in this guide of David Shiers and the 'Early Psychosis Declaration'. This used an 'imagine if ...' scenario to make the case for improvements to services for children with psychosis:

Imagine a world where ...

- People are respected and valued for their differences
- Mental Health is understood by all
- Treatment is easily understood by all
- Practitioners willingly engage with your concerns
- No-one loses their dignity
- Hospital admissions are rare
- People remain in school and work surrounded by those who care
- Hopes and dreams for the future are fullfilled
- Family/friends are informed and enabled to support a journey of recovery
- Practitioners and community workers see people as indivudals

Figure 24: *The 'imagine if...' approach*

The most successful frames create a heartfelt case for your cause from which people cannot simply walk away: 'you can check out but you can never leave'.

Here are some further examples of powerful frames that work with the explicit aim of connecting to people's sentiments and emotions:

Figures 25 and 26: *Frames that create an emotional pull*

But we know from the literature that while frames that connect emotionally are important to get people's attention, in order for people to take action frames need to 'stack up'.

If you look at successful movements you will see they also use facts and statistics to connect rationally with people's motivation - a compelling but careful case needs to be made. Reviews of successful movements show how they frequently use systematic indicators based on credible research, such as counts and analyses of hate crimes; date rape; and deaths from passive smoking. Evidence is important; people do need to be 'moved' to create a movement, but they also need to see the facts.

We can see this in the tobacco timeline (see section 8) and other examples such as the Modbury 'plastic bag free' campaign which led to Modbury in Devon becoming the first town in the British Isles to stop issuing plastic shopping bags. The 'Make Poverty History' campaign also did this very effectively, combining both an emotional and rational frame when actor Will Smith clicked his figures to represent the death, every three seconds, of a child from poverty.

▶ 5.4.3 Bridging and linking diverse groups

The next key factor in successful framing is the ability to link diverse groups together - the idea of creating bridges or a 'big tent' (but not so big that you lose focus or that you create antipathy within the group). Movements and causes need to be outward-looking and inclusive; movements that become exclusive and inward-looking become sects and elites. The Michigan Land Use Institute (MLUI), a social movement in the US, states:

> "Victories most often come when small organisations join with other groups that share similar goals. Other organisations are likely to have already developed many of the successful strategies and tools for working at the grassroots...forming coalitions is as important to success as any of the other building blocks of effective organising."

Bridging is about linking together different interest groups and movements - horizontally and vertically. A good example comes in the 'symphony of brotherhood' part of Martin Luther King's famous 'I have a dream' speech. It was used as a way of bridging with other parts of the population which were critical to the achievement of the goals of the civil rights movement:

> "Our marvellous new militancy must not lead us to a distrust of all white people. For many of our white brothers, as evidenced by their presence here today, have come to realise that their destiny is tied up with our destiny."

Other examples that readers may be familiar with include the Countryside Alliance and the recent formation of a joint government in Northern Ireland:

In the former, the pro-hunting lobby was able to mobilise a large amount of support for the essentially narrow issue of legalised fox hunting. It achieved this by framing the cause in the context of the wider rural agenda, echoing Kelman's observation that:

> "The presence in change movements of people with different conceptions of what they seek from the change is not untypical... the more a change effort is able to unite such disparate sources of power, the greater its chances of being successfully initiated."
> (Kelman, 2005)

In Northern Ireland the big breakthrough came when the negotiators (see figure 27) were able to establish the principle that all ethnic groups had equal rights, rather than viewing the issues through a 'win-lose' or 'who is the majority group?' frame.

5. FRAME TO CONNECT WITH HEARTS AND MINDS

Figure 27: *Successful framing often unites disparate sources of power*

▶ 5.4.4 Use a range of strategies

The final key factor in creating successful frames is to use a range of different strategies:

- words, stories, anecdotes and slogans
- visual images
- humor and irony
- performance and spectacle

The first set of strategies often uses the technique of juxtaposition - comparing what is being proposed to 'how it is now'. For example, micro-brewing compared small-scale craft production to mass production techniques of big beer producers; nouvelle cuisine in France was advocated by renegade chefs by comparing it to classical cuisine (Rao et al, 2001). These strategies also include speeches, meetings and interviews, songs (eg 'We shall overcome') and literature. Slogans are also important: 'Get up, stand up'.

Another really important vehicle for framing - and one that we often use unconsciously - is the 'story'. Stories and talk are the key to energy and mobilisation (Bate, 2004; Bate, 2005). When people share stories, they are alive and animated; communicating emotionally as well as verbally. Stories are also a natural mechanism of communication, and, most important here, they are the easiest route into experiences because most of them are about our experiences. You do not need a questionnaire or a survey in storytelling. Storytelling is also a social act and often collaborative or leading to collaboration. Stories also empower the storyteller - an advantage when we get patients to tell us their stories. And finally, stories also develop the imagination and stimulate creativity.

Without thinking, we will often use a story to illustrate a particular point. The conscious use and development of stories as a way of framing can be very powerful, particularly because they hit many of the buttons on the 'what makes a successful frame?' checklist. As an example, think of the power of parables which frame a complex moral or ethic in a stark and moving way. So, what stories do you have or need to develop to frame your cause? As Charon (Charon, 2003) suggests:

> "In a field of practice criticised for the many ways it can de-humanise and detach, storytelling in healthcare helps to personalise and connect."

We know patient stories are particularly powerful (Bate and Robert, 2007) and that images and visuals are also used to frame issues - anything in fact that gets people's attention. Pictures can lead to a huge shift in people's perceptions or beliefs like the photograph of Princess Diana with a patient with HIV:

Parody and humour are also very powerful framing mechanisms - if they can strike the right tone. Feminists in the 1980s used humour to reframe female stereotyping and humour is often used to reframe our views of politicians:

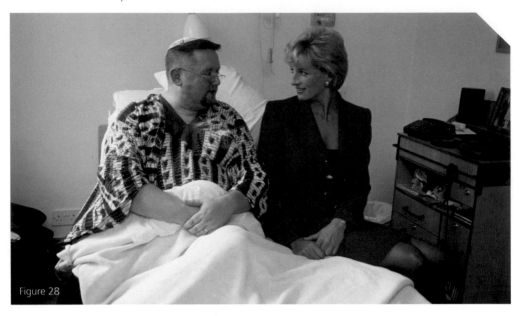

Figure 28

Modern movements often use a combination of playfulness and militancy to advance their cause (eg anti-globalisation protestors) (Whittier, 2004). Michael Moore is someone who has used humour to challenge a range of issues from globalisation and the loss of jobs; the gun lobby, Iraq and most recently healthcare:

Figures 29: *Parody and humour is a powerful framing mechanism*

Using humour, Moore has targeted General Motors and Nike executives to publicise their respective roles in plant closures in Flint, Michigan, as well as challenging sweatshops in Southeast Asia. This tactic is heavily media dependent. The effectiveness and newsworthiness of the action involves the breaking of unspoken rules about invading private space; the deliberate blurring of public and private life. For movements it is relatively low-risk and low-cost but, as Gamson (Gamson, 2004) suggests, likely to reach a point of diminishing returns if it is overused.

And there are plenty of less confrontational examples from the contemporary NHS too:

Figure 30: *Humour and NHS causes*

Performance, events and spectacles can also be useful:

Figures 31: *Example of 'spectacular' frames which aim to make a cause or issue more compelling*

However, dramatic events by themselves cannot carry a particular issue to organisational prominence, as issues must be framed in such a way that they fit within broader agenda-setting processes.

Nevertheless, the use of unconventional methods of participation is often a fundamental feature that distinguishes social movements from routine approaches (Taylor and Van Dyke, 2004). In fact movements deliberately set out to challenge normal politics and ways of doing things, often because they are unable to get their voice heard otherwise (McAdam and Snow, 1997). Some of the framing through performace might occur through costume, props, puppets and other visual images. The US-based movement, 'United for a Fair Economy' has been especially creative in this regard, using its affiliated street theatre group Class Act to dramatise the increasing gap between rich and poor in the US since the 1970s. Its satirical group Billionaires for Bush stalked the presidential candidate's electoral campaign appearances in 2000, enacting their frame in the guise of super-enthusiastic supporters (Gamson, 2004).

So what things might we do as NHS improvement leaders around our cause to make people smile rather than sneer - to disarm them and make them receptive?

6. ENERGISE AND MOBILISE

While framing is essential in building a movement, it is a strategy that might be used in any number of approaches to change and improvement. A more unique feature of a movement-based approach is the process of energising and mobilising people; getting people to 'step off the pavement', and shift from bystander to activist. So, having framed an issue in a way that gets people's attention, you then need to get their commitment and intent.

When we look across the NHS we see pockets of incredible energy and vitality around specific front-line improvement projects, where staff feel passionate and engaged in their cause of better patient care. What would it take to activate the entire 1.3 million NHS workforce in that way?

"When we look across the NHS we see pockets of incredible energy and vitality around specific frontline improvement projects, where staff feel passionate and engaged in their cause of better patient care. What would it take to activate the entire 1.3 million NHS workforce in that way?"

6.1 Passive to active

Looking at the issue of organisational performance, one publication (Loehr and Schwartz, 2003) stated that: 'Energy not time is the fuel of high performance'. Physicists talk about 'potential energy'; that is energy that is stored in objects like a stretched bow or a coiled spring. Social movement thinkers see potential energy as being stored in issues and that if only this potential energy could be released, then people would bring greater connection and commitment to the cause.

Recent healthcare improvement initiatives, such as The NHS Institute for Innovation and Improvement's The Productive Ward: Releasing Time to Care demonstrate the tremendous latent energy for change that can be released in the NHS system by a concerted focus on a specific improvement cause (NHS Institute, 2008).

Alongside energy we need mobilisation; by which we mean the process of rallying and propelling people to undertake joint action, with the aim of realising common goals (Huy, 1999). Research "suggests that the best leaders first mobilise organisational energy, then focus it" (Bruch and Ghoshal, 2003).

We tend usually in the NHS to think about engagement, but mobilisation is a step beyond that; the step that moves people from a passive to an active role, and the end point on the spectrum of participation:

engagement → commitment → mobilisation

What would a mobilised healthcare organisation look like? Perhaps it is captured in the following description:

> *"People here aren't just motivated. This isn't their job, it's a mission, it's their life; it's the cause they're committed to. For them, it's personal."* (Director, HIV AIDS programme, Albany Medical Centre, New York, as cited in Bate, Mendel and Robert, 2008)

And probably best of all the idea of mobilisation is captured in the following image and phrase:

Figure 32: *Capturing the concept of mobilisation in an image*

6. ENERGISE AND MOBILISE

▶ 6.2 What do we know about energy in healthcare?

Organisational energy is about the extent to which an organisation is able to harness the effort, speed and stamina of its workforce. From this perspective, the key task of an NHS leader is to unleash the energy of the organisation and channel it towards strategic goals. All of us seek purpose and meaning in our work, beyond using our skills and earning a living. How we feel about what is going on has an impact on our energy at work; how our work taps into our own values and sentiments; the climate our leaders create and the support they give us (Bevan, 2007).

As part of our field testing of a movement approach, we also piloted a tool developed by Stanton Marris Ltd to measure organisational energy (Stanton Marris, 2008). The tool looks at energy on two dimensions and assumes that before we can start to manage organisational energy, we need to measure it. The two critical dimensions to organisational energy, both equally important, are:

- quantum: how much energy is there in the organisation? This can be imagined as the raw fuel to power the organisation - how much comes through the door every morning?

- direction: once it is there, where does it go? Is it channelled and aligned towards achieving the goals of the organisation? Or is it dissipated in office politics, turf wars and processes and procedures for their own sake?

Using a questionnaire, Stanton Marris produce an overall Organisational Energy Index™ score for an organisation and then look at four factors that influence its organisational energy:

- connection: how far people see and feel a link between what matters to them and what matters to the organisation

- content: how far the actual tasks people do are enjoyable in themselves and challenge them

- context: how far the way the organisation operates, and the physical environment in which people work, make them feel supported

- climate: how far 'the way we do things around here' encourages people to give their best

As explained in section 1.2, more than 700 NHS staff across a wide range of NHS organisations have now taken part in the survey. There are big variations between NHS teams on the quantum and direction of energy. However, when it comes to the generation of energy, the results have been consistent across the board. 'Connection' with the core values and purpose of NHS organisations has been by far the greatest source of energy for NHS staff. 'Content', in terms of operating systems, decision-making and procedures, has been consistently the most energy-draining.

The three most consistent pieces of feedback from the Organisational Energy IndexTM are:

- "while the purpose of my organisation is worthwhile and energises me, the fact that my organisation often fails to live up to its values drains energy"

- "I am proud of the work I do and I am energised by it. However, I am not as proud of my organisation"

- "decision-making structures, processes and procedures are my biggest frustration; making shifts in these will move energy. However, this should be framed in terms of core values, not cost reduction; we don't always work in ways that maximise performance"

The results of the energy index provide some important insights into how to focus 'social movement principles in the NHS.

We should:

- focus on where the energy is to mobilise for change

- frame our causes so they tap into what people are passionate about and energised by

- avoid framing change or improvement propositions in ways that will dissipate energy

6.3 Approaches to energising and mobilising

6.3.1 Unleash and harness energy

Firstly we need to reframe the way we view the energy around us. The 2x2 matrix below looks at both intensity and quality of energy:

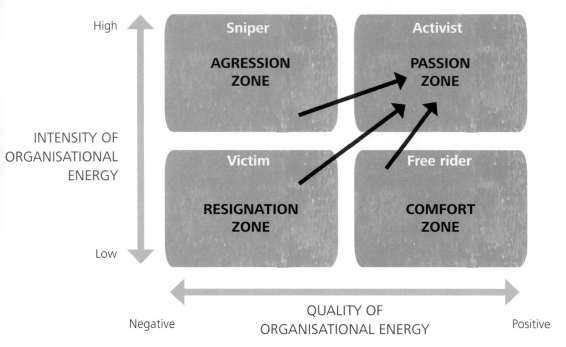

Figure 33: *Intensity and quality matrix*
Source: adapted from Bruch and Ghoshal, 2003

Often people in the aggression zone (top left) are a really important source of energy, but one which is often overlooked. In this zone, people's frustrations come out in negative ways, and unfortunately they often get labelled as blockers or 'snipers'. But actually, when you listen to what they are saying, they want many of the same things as people in the passion zone (top right, the 'activists'); it is just expressed in terms of 'what's wrong' rather than 'what's possible'. So one thing we can do is to reframe our own thinking about these people and work with them to address their frustrations. Over time we might see the negative energy becoming more positive. Thinking back to framing, we also talked about people who are disaffected – people who have effectively given up. They are represented in this model by the resignation zone (bottom left). Kelman (Kelman, 2005) observes that:

> "Discontent is likely to be present wherever rules, hierarchy and specialisation are central features of organization design".

There is so much lost energy here - as there is in the fourth quadrant: the comfort zone (bottom right). Our sense - from our work in the NHS - is that there are probably less people in the comfort zone, but even so, both these groups are a source of more energy for improvement, if we can work out how to tap into it. Kelman (Kelman, 2005) refers to this as 'activating the discontented'.

One way of thinking about tapping into these groups is through the concept of discretionary effort. Studies by the Hay Group have shown that there are very different levels of productivity from branches of offices all working to the same resourcing levels, delivering the same outputs. Their conclusion is that different levels of productivity can only be explained through the idea of discretionary effort, ie the extra amount that individuals give when they are engaged and motivated by what they do. This is summed up in the phrase, 'work is contractual, effort is personal'.

In NHS improvement efforts, we need to think about how we can tap into the discretionary effort of people in the comfort zone and in the resignation zone, and we will only do this by understanding how we can connect with them on a personal level; what needs to be different for them to come to the table? The following case study is drawn from one of our field test sites and shows how social movements thinking might help.

▶ **Case study: Pat and Katrina's story**

Two NHS midwives, Pat and Katrina, took part in our first field test of the social movements approach. The following are extracts taken from the diary they kept.

"My name is Katrina and this is Pat. We work as labour ward midwives in a busy maternity unit in England. We have approx 3,500 deliveries a year. The unit comprises of a labour ward, a postnatal\antenatal ward, a day assessment unit, an antenatal clinic and a community based unit. There are approximately 120 members of staff."

....

"We were first introduced to social movement on 6th December 2006. Our initial response was of suspicion which then turned to intrigue and then to action."

....

6th December:
We managed to muster up four members of staff to attend a meeting that the whole unit had been invited to. We had just finished a busy stressful day, with no break and all we wanted to do was go home, but our divisional manager, clinical director and someone from the NHS Institute of Innovation and Improvement were coming to talk to us about something called social movement - whatever that is! To top it all they turned up late, well it was late as far as we were concerned because we were actually due to finish at 3pm and it was now 3.10. We were about to go when they all arrived.

"It had never occurred to us before, but we suddenly realised the way we felt must have a knock-on effect to the women we care for"

A bit of background here, we had been told a couple of weeks before that the hospital was financially in debt. For us that meant that our antenatal ward had to close because we couldn't afford to staff it. We could no longer supplement our staff with extra midwives if we were short and morale across the unit was rock bottom. We were always being told to do things better and whatever we did never seemed to be good enough.

Now we are being told that if we work on things together we can make anything happen and management will not be involved. To be honest we didn't know what the woman from the Institute was talking about. We were suspicious and cynical about it all. She said that she would meet up with us the same time next week, if we wanted to come back. Was this just another way of management to get us do something for nothing or are we being offered something worth looking at?

Pat and I did however go away and decided together that if I did it she would do it. After all, what did we have to lose? Nothing could get any worse. We decided we would come back and over the next few days we would look at things we could change. Most importantly, we needed to think what we could do about morale amongst the staff.

"This was a pivotal moment for me as it became obvious from the other teams present that no one had thought of looking at improving staff morale before starting to improve the service we provide. It felt as if we had hit on something that could help to improve other areas of the NHS".

13th December:
We manage to persuade 15 members of staff to attend, we were all curious to see what social movement was about. The oddest thing about this meeting was that we were being told that in fact we were actually doing very well as a unit, that we were great individuals, we have a strong mix of talent and skills, few formal complaints and good national performance.

At the meeting we then started to open up and tell them of how we really felt, about the negativity, the low morale and how the continual criticism we received from everyone made us feel. This feeling of being able to off-load our feelings and for someone to actually listen to us felt good. It had never occurred to us before, but we suddenly realised the way we felt must have a knock-on effect to the women we care for.

Having our divisional manager there was a real bonus because she could advise us of quick ways we could use to make things happen and stop us worrying about getting permission. We left the meeting excited and motivated and immediately started looking at ways to improve our environment, morale and our patient experience.

27th December:
Despite it being the Christmas period, 18 members of staff attended the meeting including some community midwives, who were now taking ownership of the new weekend postnatal drop-in, where new mothers can attend at the weekend for support and advice This was introduced to save money, but both midwives and parents are making every use of it and enjoying the experience. It was a very positive meeting. We were beginning to get a few staff from different areas of the unit which was great news. We decided to free up some cupboard space on labour ward, develop an exit questionnaire, pilot our new staff room for three months, convert the old staff room to a temporary admission room and move the Day Assessment Unit to the closed antenatal ward - Yes we had developed quite a list of things we wanted to change!

10th January:
We were surprised to find 30 members of staff, most of whom were from the postnatal ward and attending their first meeting. This feels good again as news is spreading and others want to get involved.

22nd January:
Our meetings continue every Wednesday. Pat and I are asked to attend a field test workshop in Coventry. This was a pivotal moment for me as it became obvious from the other teams present that no one had thought of looking at improving staff morale before starting to improve the service we provide. It felt as if we had hit on something that could help to improve other areas of the NHS.

28th January:
Over the last couple of weeks, there has been a buzz - morale is improving and staff are working on their areas having heard what we have done on labour ward. Our manager is happier and helping us with our cause – which is great for us. Every so often I see the enthusiasm in someone that I had back at the beginning and that is so encouraging.

31st January:
Staff from the postnatal ward are beginning to get on board. They started off by telling us of the negativity on their ward and that they never receive positive feedback.. It was so similar to the first time when we opened up. We said that they had to work on ways to change this before anything positive could come out of it. I suggested that the ward managers attend our meetings to help bridge the differences we all had with them. The postnatal ward staff did however, by the end of the meeting, begin to work their way round this negativity and were looking at ways they could change this feeling of helplessness. After the meeting I approached the postnatal ward manager to invite her to our meetings. She said she would be happy to do this when she could.

End of March:
Throughout the rest of February and March our meetings were on the whole positive and everyone was given a chance to put their views forward and then we would all discuss them. Setbacks continued to happen but we found ways to overcome them in the end. We now have a core group from each area who continue to strive to work towards improvements with the help of their colleagues.
We have decided to have an away day at the end of April. Between us we have identified a few key people from each of our 5 teams to work together. We will look at improving the women's experience in different areas of the service, but also the staff, we cannot forget the staff. We have already done some work to come up with the biggest opportunities to make improvements and fix things – things that we really need to work together on. We've invited the ward managers and a couple of the doctors so we can take it forward together after the event. Pat and I continue to support each other when either of us have had enough and take it in turn to chair the meetings.

In Pat and Katrina's story we can see how their discretionary effort started from the resignation zone, becoming more positive, as they began to believe in their ability to make a difference. Time and time again in our NHS social movement work, we encounter groups of staff who are sitting on huge reserves of untapped energy. They are suppressed by short-term performance targets and top-down models of change that are coercion and compliance-based, rather than collaborative and partnership-based. In this context, our role as improvement leaders is to unleash the energy of the staff and channel it towards improvement goals, utilising our full range of improvement tools and approaches.

Another huge source of additional energy is patients and carers:

"The biggest untapped resources in the health system are not doctors but users. We need systems that allow people and patients to be recognised as producers and participants, not just receivers of systems... At the heart of the approach, users will play a far larger role in helping to identify needs, propose solutions, test them out and implement them, together." (Design Council, 2004)

However, even in the more progressive health systems, thinking about engaging patients tends to be quite passive - typically 'getting their views' through listening and responding (see figure 34). However, health organisations that have mobilised patients so that they are directly working on an improvement agenda have found they have in turn energised staff and delivered significant results.

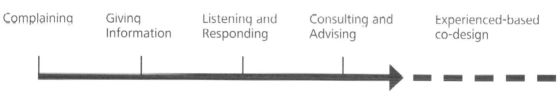

| Complaining | Giving Information | Listening and Responding | Consulting and Advising | Experienced-based co-design |

Figure 34. *The spectrum of involvement*
Source: Bate and Robert, 2007

At the far right of the figure is an approach called 'experience-based co-design' (EBD); the development of which was supported by the NHS Institute for Innovation and Improvement (NHS Institute 2009) it has yielded some impressive results in terms of bringing energy to improvement efforts:

"The...contribution of EBD... is in showing how and where a change or improvement effort finds the energy to bring about and then sustain the change: the core issue of mobilisation... it is important to distinguish between commitment, engagement, and mobilisation. The first is the equivalent to being committed to climb on the change "bus"; the second to putting it into gear; and the third to actually moving it down the road - the issue of practical action. All too often... we see the first two but not the third. The great strength of EBD... is that once staff and patients have come together face to face on a regular basis; have listened to each others' stories and experiences, shared their moving videos; and have had some (serious) fun with scissors and paper in prototyping new solutions, they find it difficult to walk away with the job incomplete. Change, making things better, making a difference - takes on the status of an imperative."
(Bate and Robert, 2007)

Y●UR EXPERIENCE MATTERS

PATIENTS AND STAFF DESIGNING SERVICES TOGETHER.

The aim
We want to work with patients, carers and staff to design the best possible care experience for head and neck cancer patients. The first step is to find out what you like and don't like about the service.

How will we achieve this?
We would like to learn more about how the service looks through your eyes, by listening to your stories and experiences. What is learnt from your experiences will be used to decide what improvements to make.

Who will decide what improvements if any should be made and how an improved service should look?
A group of patients, carers and staff with a small team of health care design researchers will decide together. The patient and staff group will use the main points from the stories to design a service that keeps the good parts of the experience and reduces those that spoil it.

How can I help and what would this involve?
You can help by meeting with one or two of the health care design researchers to tell them about your experience. Later you could also be part of the patient, carer and staff group helping to decide what improvements to make.

You are under no pressure to talk to the team if you do not want to and your decision will not affect your care.

If you want to know more about this ask a member of the Head and Neck team or contact
Elaine Hide : 01582 497417 ext:7417 Elaine.Hide@ldh.nhs.uk

Carole Glover : (Specialist Head and Neck Nurse)
0845 1270127 ext:8038 Carole.Glover@ldh.nhs.uk

The Luton and Dunstable Hospital **NHS**
Associated Teaching Hospital of the University of London   NHS Trust

In partnership with: *Institute for Innovation and Improvement* **NHS**

Figure 35: *Poster advertising the EBD approach in one of the early pilot sites*

▶ 6.3.2 Build commitment and connection

So, having found the energy and tapped into it, we now need to build a connection between the cause and the people we are aiming to reach. Another key approach to mobilising, therefore, is to build commitment and connection. From the Organisational Energy IndexTM results referred to earlier, it is evident that there is often a great deal of disconnection between staff within the NHS and the goals of their organisations. And yet, if we are going to get mobilisation around a cause, (ie we are going to see people take concrete actions in the direction of change) we need to make connections between them and the cause we are working on, and we need to get their commitment. One way of thinking about this is in terms of moving people along a spectrum - running through 'obstructing - no commitment - let it happen - help it happen - make it happen':

Key Players	No Commitment	Let It Happen	Help It Happen	Make It Happen
1.		X ———————————→		O
2.		X ————→ O		
3.		X ———————————→		O
4.		O	X	
5.			XO	
6.	X ————→ O			
7.		X ———————————→		O
8.		XO		
9.	X ———————————→		O	
10.			O ←——— X	

Figure 36: *Commitment spectrum*
Source. Beckhard and Harris (1987),
Organization Transitions. Managing Complex Change

Typically, in the NHS we seek as a minimum to ensure we move the people from 'obstructing' to 'let it happen', and assume that the centrally-driven structures will be sufficient to drive through the change required. However, a movement approach would be seeking to get people into the 'make it happen' category, to the point where they are so dissatisfied with the current state that they are committed to changing to a future state. How we move people along this spectrum will depend on effective framing of our cause to connect and build commitment. From the evidence we know that connection and commitment come from appealing to feelings, sentiments and values - 'tapping into sentiment pools', or:

> "If you want to build a ship do not gather men together and assign tasks. Instead teach them the longing for the wide endless sea." (Saint Exupery, Little Prince)

Three approaches to forging a deeper commitment are the use of mobilising narratives; 'authentic voices'; and 'hot-housing'.

6. ENERGISE AND MOBILISE

Mobilising narratives

Let us look at mobilising narratives first. These are essentially stories that have a clarity, a truth and a passion that will move people. Stories play a key role in the formation and maintenance of social movements:

> "Social movements... are created by the stories people tell to themselves and one another. They reflect the deepest ways in which people understand who they are and to whom they are connected. Whatever they are, and whatever historical sources of their development, they are constructed from the intermeaning of personal and social biographies from the narratives people rehearse to themselves about the nature of their lives." (Kling, 1995)

Perhaps the greatest power of the story is its power to move people - which is what we mean by the phrase the 'mobilising narrative'. One illustration is a story that Barbara Monroe, the Chief Executive of St. Christopher's Hospice in South London, relates about a young dying woman and her family (as cited in Bate and Robert, 2007):

> ". . . a young woman with breast cancer, multiple secondaries, and her husband and two children. She says, "I don't want to die in hospital". He says, "I don't think she should have any more chemotherapy". She is trying every experimental treatment she can at the local hospital because she wants to carry on living. She's got kids. He says, "She won't face it, we need a nanny now, because she's going blind", because she's got secondaries just behind her eyes. She says, "Can I trust him with the children? I need to stay alive for as long as possible".

One day when I was visiting them, they completely knocked me over because she looked at me and she said, "Have you got any suggestions for improving our sex life?" This is a woman who has had a double mastectomy, who is skeletal, who has got a problem with uncontrolled vomiting. I was not even thinking about their sex life or that they were thinking about their sex life, but for them this was a really important way of staying connected as a couple.

They had two children: "Why can't the nurses make her better?" Despite the fact that she wanted to die at home, in fact, her brain secondaries in the last two or three days of her life meant that in the end her husband decided that he could not continue to look after her at home. The children were with her and in her room at the hospice when she died, and the room was a four-bedded bay. I shall never forget being with these two children, aged four and six, and the four-year-old said, "She's resting". The six-year-old said very loudly, "No, she's not, she's snuffed it". And there are three other dying people just beyond the curtains and I thought, "Oh, how do you make this okay?" In fact, the other three people, when I went to talk to them, all said how glad they were that these children were able to be with their mum at such an important time.

Next day they are visiting, they are going to collect the death certificate, they are going to pick up mum's belongings, and they visit mum's body: "Is she completely dead? Will she still be dead when I'm 10, when I'm 15? Why is daddy crying? Why is mummy cold?" We'd just got mummy out of our fridge and the kids were touching her. And then they look at their dad and they say, "Will you keep one side of the bed for mummy's ghost?" This man who is grieving, who has just had his wife die, also has to try and manage his children and their very practical questions. It was just before Christmas. Kids know that daddy will not get the Christmas presents right. "Can we come to the funeral? 'What happens when your heart stops? When will daddy die? Who is more important, God or Jesus? What are spirits? Who goes to Hell?'".

As it happens, these kids had a cat that was called Black Cat, and by a horrible coincidence Black Cat had cancer. And just to remind us that there is not some recipe book of skills, and I have been in the business for quite a long time, these kids looked at me and said, "They are going to kill Black Cat. Nobody put mummy to sleep. Why don't they put people to sleep if they put animals to sleep?" I didn't know the answer to that so I said, "I don't know".

Mobilising narratives do not need to be over prepared and planned, but they do need to come from the heart. Their power often comes from their freshness and spontaneity.

Authentic voices

Another approach to making an emotional connection and forging commitment is to use 'authentic voices': first-hand accounts of experiences of a particular event or situation. The notion behind this drew on the 'Movement to end child abuse and neglect' in the US. This was a coalition of more than 30 national health and child abuse organizations and over 3,000 individual members who were committed to mobilising two million authentic voices (survivors) and supporters across the country (National Call to Action, 2007).

One other very powerful example of the use of authentic voices is the Oscar-winning film - Born into Brothels:

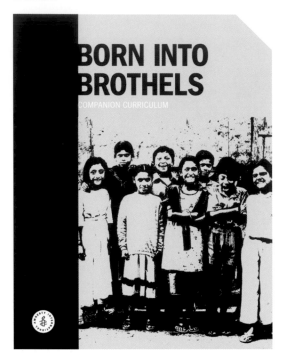 

Figure 37: *Powerful use of authentic voices in film*

Born into Brothels: Calcutta's Red Light Kids is a 2004 film about the children of prostitutes in Sonagachi, Calcutta's red light district. It began when a documentary photographer went to Kolkata (Calcutta) to photograph prostitutes. While there, she befriended their children and offered to teach the children photography to reciprocate being allowed to photograph their mothers. The children were given cameras so they could learn photography and possibly improve their lives. Much of their work was used in the film, and the filmmakers recorded the classes as well as daily life in the red light district. The children's work was exhibited, and one boy was even sent to a photography conference in Amsterdam.

In Born into Brothels: Calcutta's Red Light Kids the power of the film clearly lies in the fact that children speak in the first person. The perspectives are their own and through these voices and images they share their world view with the audience. Often commentators overlay powerful and emotive stories such as this with their own interpretations and assumptions. By using the authentic voice in a mobilising narrative, the filmmaker makes an emotional connection for the viewer between the individual and the subject matter.

This technique has been used to great effect in our improvement efforts in the NHS Institute – by nurses filming their own work on wards for the improvement programme Releasing Time to Care – and by patients mapping their own emotional journey through our healthcare systems in Experience Based Design.

'Hot-housing'

If your cause is going to be attractive to people, it needs to generate energy and pull people into it. Leaders need to think about how they can hold energising events and meetings that make people want to take part. Social movement researchers describe this in the following terms:

> *"A small cadre of professionals play the role of activists, involving workers and managers in training sessions and problem-solving teams. The hope is that positive feedback between the converted and the unconverted will lead new behaviours to diffuse and become self-sustaining."* (Strang and Jung, 2002)

David Shiers (see case study in section 1) developed a process that he calls 'hot-housing': two-day events that take people out of their usual environment and helps them to focus on the issues in hand. In David's words "'hot housing' is the creation of a local environment that encourages the rapid growth and development of someone or something, in an intense way."

This intensity can help build momentum around the cause and increase people's preparedness to take action.

▶ 6.3.3 Building mass

The final challenge to address as we think about mobilisation is how do we build mass? How do we shift from a small group of enthusiasts to a mass movement? There are a number of concrete strategies that movements employ to build mass:

- recruitment strategies: explicit action to get people to sign up
- campaigns: to get people to take a specific action
- application of 'tipping points' principles.

Recruitment

Looking at recruitment, evidence shows that the first key strategy, particularly in terms of getting a cause off the ground, is to target the 'right sort of people' - the people that you know have a high probability of sharing your values; have a history of previous 'activism'; and are part of wider networks that are likely to support your cause. This is expressed by Marwell who states:

> *"Collective action happens when a critical mass of interested and resourceful individuals can co-ordinate their efforts... successful organising is more a matter of whom you can mobilise than of how many you can mobilise."* (Marwell, Oliver and Prahl, 1988)

Then, once an initial core group of committed individuals has formed, the challenge is to reach out and bring in a wider group - people that may be in the comfort zone, the aggression zone, or the resignation zone (figure 33). An important strategy to employ when doing this is the 'homophily' principle which is built on the recognition that most human communication will occur between a source and a receiver who are alike (ie have a common frame of reference). The evidence also shows that individuals who depart from the homophily principle and attempt to communicate with others who are different from them often face the frustration of ineffective communication. This is not just because they may lack a 'connection', but also because differences in technical competence, social status, beliefs and language, can lead to mistakes in meaning, thereby, causing messages to be distorted or to go unheeded. So, in a healthcare context, we are much more likely to win people to our cause if we build peer-to-peer communication and recruitment; medic-to-medic, nurse-to-nurse and so on. The implication of this is the importance of getting a broad church amongst your initial supporters so that you have the ability to reach out in a number of directions.

"It had never occurred to us before, but we suddenly realised the way we felt must have a knock-on effect to the women we care for"

A good illustration of the use of homophily is Jamie Oliver's 'School Dinners' campaign. Although Jamie Oliver was a key 'leader' from the public perspective, the success of the campaign is in large part down to the fact that he had a dinner lady to lead it with him. Alone, If the dinner ladies were not on board with the message, then it would have been very unlikely that schools would have pushed the changes through.

Interestingly, Jamie Oliver also ran his own version of a 'hothouse'; a camp for dinner ladies where they had some intensive training and a chance to network and build alliances. The other strategy that is often employed around national causes and campaigns is the use of celebrities. The image below is particularly powerful because it manages to combine the celebrity with the 'authentic voice' - the young woman Birhan Weldu who had previously become known to hundreds of millions of viewers of 'Live Aid' as a starving child.

Of course, involving celebrities of this magnitude in local NHS issues is relatively unlikely, but it is worth considering who are the 'celebrities' in our context whose endorsement and involvement will move other people to get involved.

We also know that personal attendance and involvement is crucial to recruitment; get people to come along half the battle has been won. (See for example McAdam's description of how the experience of Freedom Summer's orientation camps had a defining influence on the idealistic middle class youth membership – McAdam, 1988).

6. ENERGISE AND MOBILISE

Campaigns

Another way of building mass is through campaign approaches - another specific tactic frequently used in social movements. The Michigan Land Use Institute (MLUI) says:

> *"The heart of a successful campaign is how effective a group's messages are, and how well they are communicated and disseminated."* (MLUI, 2007)

Campaigns can be a highly-effective way of building mass around a cause. But it is important to recognise that a campaign is not, in itself, a movement. In everyday life people are surrounded by campaigns - some of which will successfully move people from being bystanders to being participants. Examples of successful campaigns include: 'Drink Driving' 'Clunk-clink every trip' and 'Back to sleep':

Figure 38: *Image from the Foundation for the Study of Infant Deaths Cot Death Campaign stickers, illustrator Julie Anderson*

One excellent example from the US healthcare sector is the '5 Million Lives Campaign' which ran from December 2006 to December 2008. It created a level of engagement that was unprecedented in the healthcare industry globally. As many as 3,924 US hospitals took part, representing around 80% of US hospital beds. They worked on up to 12 interventions (mainly targeting reduction in infections, medication errors and surgical complications) in a shared effort to avoid five million patient injuries in US hospitals (McCannon, forthcoming). –

Don Berwick, CEO of the Institute for Healthcare Improvement (IHI) is the leader of these campaigns. He said: 'I'm losing my patience'. The healthcare system, he added, is not working and it's not improving fast enough. So what does he do? He organises a campaign. This is an interesting extract from the IHI website (www.ihi.org):

> "Who is IHI? It's a difficult question. Sometimes we have trouble answering it our selves. IHI is a unique organisation that defies simple definition ... most of all, IHI is YOU. IHI is not an organisation with walls; it is really more of concept - a movement for collaboration and change. And that is only possible to the extent that change-minded people and organisations are part of the work".

On the website, you will also find reference to campaign materials, campaign brochures, videos, field operations guides and more, all available for downloading. Someone needs to produce these materials; planners are needed at head office to put together these resources and organise the campaign. This is just an illustration of how traditional 'planners' can apply themselves in different ways through a campaign-based approach.

Figure 39: *Example materials for a campaign-based approach*

6. ENERGISE AND MOBILISE

Application

Effective campaigns need a great deal of planning, organising and resources in terms of time and often money. However, the right campaign at the right time can be hugely effective. The literature shows that there are five key elements to a successful campaign.

- Firstly the campaign message needs to make sense to people and have a relevance to their everyday context. On this theme, activist Saul Alinsky said:

> "a new idea must be at the least couched in the language of past ideas; often, it must be, at first, diluted with vestiges of the past."
> (Alinsky, 1972)

Going back to the anti-tobacco campaign highlighted earlier, the Government's decision to ban smoking fits with the zeitgeist and has met with surprisingly little opposition – there have been no campaigns or rallies of aggrieved smokers, publicans, 'working men's club' committees - whereas something like the proposed 'Home Information Packs' (where prospective house sellers are legally required to provide information about their home to prospective purchasers) failed to tune into the zeitgeist and lacked the relevance to people's everyday lives. The packs consequently had to be delayed and amended.

- Secondly, a campaign also needs a strategic theme as this will create the forward momen tum; people need to see the campaign message as a step in a journey, not a narrowly-focused task (see below for example).

- Thirdly, within the strategic theme there still needs to be some small, single issues to work on; something so that people can see that they can make a difference and take action. A great example of how these two elements have been combined is in the Modbury 'plastic bag free' campaign. There is a strategic theme - reduce pollution to protect wildlife - but also a very specific action, stop using plastic bags:

Figure 40: *Modbury's 'plastic bag free' campaign combines a strategic theme and smaller actions*

- Fourthly, the campaign needs to have an inclusive approach; that is, anyone can join in as long as they are committed to the cause. For example, more radical groups (such as radical feminism) often fail to build the mass and momentum around their cause because they exclude potential allies.

- Fifthly and finally, there needs to be an infrastructure to ensure continued participation. So, for example, if you look as the website for the Countryside Alliance (or indeed the IHI website mentioned earlier) you will see a strong infrastructure to support continued involvement and participation.

If any of these five key elements are missing, campaigns can fail as shown in figure 41. For example, if campaign leaders are not paying attention and responding to everyday concerns, the campaign can become just a form of social engineering; or if the campaign lacks an infrastructure then it is likely to lose momentum.

Listening	Strategic theme	Single issue	Sweeping people in	Infrastructure	**Failure modes**
?	■	■	■	■	= social engineering
■	?	■	■	■	= opportunism, diffusion of effort and lack of direction
■	■	?	■	■	= lack of focus and impact; does not connect locally
■	■	■	?	■	= political resistance
■	■	■	■	?	= loss of momentum, enabling organisation

Figure 41: *Common ways a campaign can fail*
(adapted from Hirschhorn and May, 2000)

Evidence shows that the ommission of any one of the five elements (Listening, Strategic Theme, Single Issue, Sweeping people in, Infrastructure) recommended for the mounting of a successful campaign can result in the failure modes listed in the right hand column of the table above.

6. ENERGISE AND MOBILISE

'Tipping Point' principles

Finally, one last set of strategies to think about are the themes from Malcom Gladwell's concept of the 'tipping point' (Gladwell, 2002). Gladwell observes the phenomena of seemingly sudden significant changes in attitudes or behaviours (rather than specific social movements). Although it is not part of the body of social movement literature, there are some interesting lessons that might be applied. He talks about three key factors:

• the power of the few: the influencing abilities of a small number of people whose opinions carry weight because either they are connectors or knowledgeable

• the 'stickiness of the message': how effectively the message takes hold; again 'Back to Sleep' (figure 38) is a good example of a 'sticky' message, and

• the power of context: to what extent the surrounding context promotes or inhibits a particular behaviour or change.

▶ 6.4 A closing word about leaders and energy

Organisational leaders are stewards of organisational energy (Bevan, 2007). As formal or informal leaders, clinical or managerial, we are a high 'leverage point' for energy. Our behaviours are magnified and have a bigger impact than those of other people. We inspire or demoralise others by how well we mobilise, focus, invest and sustain their collective energy. In fact, recent research points to a clear relationship between leadership performance and ability to energise (Gratton, 2007). 'Energising' leaders get better results by attracting more effort from those around them, and by attracting other high performers. Their ideas are more likely to be adopted by others.

As activist-leaders, we need the courage to make a personal stand for what is right. We need to challenge the status quo as necessary and tackle the tough issues. We need to believe that a different future is possible and that the people we work with and serve have the capability, energy and motivation to deliver the changes. Critically, we need to be able to preserve this optimism, often against the odds. As Don Berwick of IHI put it:

"Question: What is the single most important thing we can do to improve health care?

Answer: Get as many leaders as we can find who show optimism and confidence."

7. ORGANISE FOR IMPACT

The organise for impact principle looks, on the face of it, somewhat out of keeping with a social movement approach to large-scale change. This is because the role of organisation in social movements often goes un-noticed; there is a common misperception that movements are entirely spontaneous, unorganised and unplanned. This could not be further from the case: most movements are underpinned by highly- effective forms of organisation (good examples highlighted earlier are the campaigns led by the IHI where success was built on the kind of organisation that typifies many other successful movements and campaigns). Reviews of the movement literature consistently emphasise the importance of organisation (or 'mobilising structure') on various other aspects of movement formation and maintenance.

In some respects the idea of 'organisation' sounds fairly traditional. After all, that is what organisations do. But the approach to organisation in movements comes from a very different perspective to traditional approaches. Nonetheless, movements do have to be organised; it is this organisation which, firstly, translates energy and passion into purposeful, effective action, and secondly, enables the movement to stay in existence through necessary co-ordination and resourcing:

> "There is absolutely no question about the fact that social movement activity is organised in some fashion or another. Clearly there are different forms of organisation and degrees of organisation (eg tightly coupled -v- loosely coupled)... but to note such differences is not grounds for dismissing the significance of organisation to social movements."
> (Snow et al, 2004)

▶ 7.1 Why is organisation important?

For a movement to survive, activists must be able to create an enduring organisational structure to sustain collective action. But the form of movement organisation differs from 'organisations' as we tend to know them in healthcare. For example, whereas most of our 'organisation' in the NHS is about planning, control and stability, organisers of movements are more concerned with opportunism, mobilisation and change. In short, 'right brain' rather than left.

As figure 12 shows, organisational structures are traditionally led by positional leaders (such as executive sponsors), whereas movements are led by activists. Furthermore, while we in healthcare traditionally like to have clear project plans with timelines and milestones, movements have a clear cause but are less specific about how they will go about reaching it; they can not commit to timescales, and there is an unpredictability about what might happen and when. In short, 'action' not 'planning' is the focus of movement organisers - the notion of organising for action. Finally, organisation of movements is wisdom or knowledge driven, whereas, in organisations, we usually build structures around hierarchy.

7. ORGANISE FOR IMPACT

Figure 42: *How organisational tactics differ between traditional and movement approaches*

Traditional tactics	Movement tactics
Executive sponsor	Activist
Project Board, project teams etc	Core team, voluntary, connectors
Defined deliverables and process	Big aim - open approach
Project plan, targets, measurable timescales, etc	Simple rules, opportunistic, go with energy, tipping point, unpredictable
Board reports, minutes, reporting structure, monitoring	Celebrations, communication, blogs
Seeking approval	Empowered to get on with it
Hierarchical	Sapiential (based on wisdom)

Source: NHS Institute (2008)

Of course, this is not to say that traditional tactics are not right in the right circumstances. For clearly-defined outcomes for which it is possible to control the relevant factors, a programme approach is often appropriate. But when the aim is something that is highly- dependent on the behaviour of many disparate individuals, a programmatic approach becomes futile.

7.2 Key approaches to successful organising

7.2.1 Form a core team

The first key element in 'organising for impact' is to create a distributed leadership model. This means that leadership is not vested in one individual, but across a core team and 'tiered', ie through 'nodes' or local branches. There are typically four tiers to consider:

• core team
• extended core team
• bridge leaders
• local organisers.

For example, the 'Patient Safety First' campaign (the national patient safety campaign in England) used this organising structure with a multi-tiered leadership system:

Campaign Infrastructure

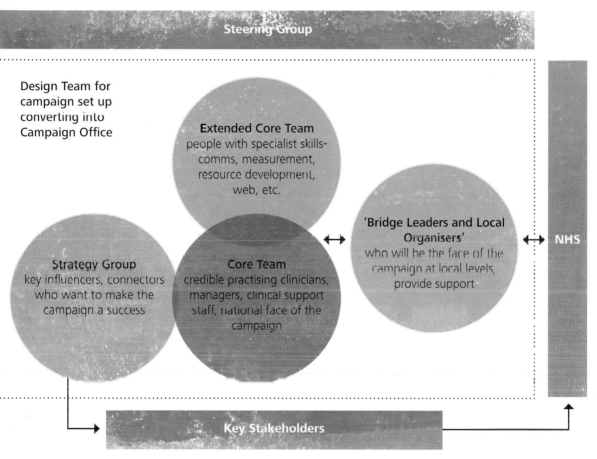

Steering Group

Design Team for campaign set up converting into Campaign Office

Extended Core Team
people with specialist skills-comms, measurement, resource development, web, etc.

'Bridge Leaders and Local Organisers'
who will be the face of the campaign at local levels, provide support

NHS

Strategy Group
key influencers, connectors who want to make the campaign a success

Core Team
credible practising clinicians, managers, clinical support staff, national face of the campaign

Key Stakeholders

Figure 43: *Patient Safety First's organising structure*

7. ORGANISE FOR IMPACT

In this structure, there is a core team responsible for being the national face of the campaign, supported by an extended team of people with specialist skills and knowledge – for instance, measurement, communications and safety. At local level, these core team members are being networked with people who have volunteered to take an active role in the campaign as local organisers, in order to build a strong grass roots movement. The campaign as a whole is supported by a strategy group that brings together the people able to advise on actions that help create the conditions necessary for success.

At the heart of a movement is a core leadership team rather than an individual leader (Disney and Gelb, 2000; Ganz, 2000):

> *"Movements are more likely to succeed if they attract leadership teams with diverse back grounds, skills and viewpoints. Quality decisions are likely to emerge from a collective of such leaders who set the creative process in motion through concerted deliberations and brainstorming."* (Ganz, 2000)

The role of this core team is essential to the organisation of the movement. It is important to agree roles and the division of labour between members of the core team; without this the initial energy that has been generated will be unfocused and likely to fizzle out. Dividing up the work between people will also reduce the chances of burn-out:

> *"In too many cases, promising grass roots movements fail because too few people do most of the work. Burn out is an occupational hazard in community organising. Successful groups develop the organisational capacity to spread the work around."* (MLUI)

Looking more closely at the core team's role, there are some key responsibilities. The first grouping of responsibilities is around the 'positioning' of the cause. Not surprisingly an important part of this is the responsibility for framing - building the platform, constructing the rational case, creating the narrative of the cause and then capturing and describing the journey being travelled:

In addition, the core team also needs to create a sense of collective identity around the cause and wider movement, while fostering commitment, and from these beginnings, building a community.

The second group of key roles is around 'activating' - supporting action at a localised level. This is not about directing local teams and participants, but about orchestrating, facilitating and enabling. Doing this successfully will require the core team to have a sound understanding of the local context(s) in which the cause is being supported. The core team needs to keep a 'helicopter view' of what is happening and to seek opportunities to shape and build on successes, rather than to try to control local activities.

The core team also needs to legitimise local action through rewards and incentives and provide 'safe havens' - essentially neutral areas where people can begin to engage and speak freely about hopes and concerns. Whyte (Whyte, 1994) talks about this concept in the context of finding the soul:

> "... all of us are familiar with frantic busyness as a state that continually precludes us from opening to the quiet and contemplation it takes to be smart .... We do not even have time to find out if our momentum is taking us over the nearest cliff. If we are serious about the soul at work, and the creativity that sustains a soulful work life, all of us must confront the question of quiet and contemplation in the workplace".

The third key responsibility of the core team is in mobilising the wider organisational structures to support local action, and thereby promote spread. This includes securing resources - what social movements scholars call 'resource mobilisation' (Zald and McCarthy, 1987). These could be resources like knowledge, skills, or time (ie not just financial). The team also needs to convey a sense of urgency and facilitate access and influence into key structures and individuals, linking the movement to the wider society.

Movements are typically organised by the sort of small core team that keeps close to the issues and progress. The tight-knit grouping helps maintain pace. However, they also need to tap into an 'extended core team' to draw in other perspectives and expertise. For example, as Platt and Lilley (Platt and Lilley, 1994) show in their analysis of letters written to Martin Luther King, his second tier of leaders mobilised thousands of youths to engage in demonstrations when King was out of town, this is what saved the day in the 1963 civil rights campaign in Birmingham:

> "his followers were not passive devotees. They were participants and leaders at different levels of the movement, and many of them offered strategic advice to King"
> (Morris and Staggenborg, 2002)

Another excellent example of mobilisation from a movement campaign perspective is the Barack Obama election campaign. This is the email that Obama sent to many tens of thousands of supporters on the evening of his election victory:

From: Barack Obama [mail to: info@barackobama.com]
Sent: Tuesday, November 04, 2008, 10:19pm
To: Richard XXX
Subject: How this happened

Richard -

I'm about to head to Grant Park to talk to everyone gathered there, but I wanted to write to you first.

We just made history.

And I don't want to forget how we did it.

You made history every single day during this campaign – every day you knocked on doors, made a donation, or talked to your family, friends and neighbours about why you believe it's time for a change.

I want to thank all of you who gave your time, talent, passion to this campaign.

We have a lot of work to do to get our country back on track, and I'll be in touch soon about what comes next.

But I want to be very clear about one thing …

All of this happened because of you.

Thank you.

Barack

Figure 44: *Obama's email to campaign supporters*

The Obama campaign used mobilisation strategies and channels through new media that had never been utilised or exploited previously. This note is typical. It makes a very personal connection, yet it makes that connection to an entire national movement of people. It demonstrates very effectively 'the power of one, the power of many'.

▶ 7.2.2 Bridge leaders

There need to be local organisers that take forward action on the frontline and there also needs to be 'bridge leaders' between the core team and these local activists - leaders that can effectively translate messages across the tiers. Bridge leaders are:

> "those neighbourhood and community organis ers who mediate between top leadership and the vast bulk of followers, turning dreams and grand plans into on-the-ground realities". (Goldstone, 2001).

Some clinical leaders play very special and effective roles as 'bridge leaders' in the NHS. Most change is based on the homiphily principle and spread peer-to-peer; doctor-to-doctor, nurse-to-nurse, and so on. It is much more difficult for a managerial leader to win a clinician to a cause than it is for a fellow clinician. However, in every NHS organisation there is a core group of clinical leaders who are able to operate in both worlds, clinical and managerial. They are able to frame the managerial message into a clinical perspective. They are often amongst the most effective movement-type leaders in our organisations.

"in every NHS organisation there is a core group of clinical leaders who are able to operate in both worlds, clinical and managerial. They are able to frame the managerial message into a clinical perspective. They are often amongst the most effective movement-type leaders in our organisations"

▶ 7.2.2 Networks as organising structures

Essentially, networks are the mechanisms through which groups seek to organise; they are the collective building blocks of social movements:

> "If we have learned anything from the last twenty five years of social movement research, it is that movements do not depend on interest or opportunity alone, but build on indi enous social networks in domestic societies... it is more due to networks of people who are linked to each other by a specific interpersonal bond, than to formal organisation or ind vidual incentives, that collective action is aggregated". (McAdam et al, 1995)

Networks are crucial mechanisms for building collective identity that fulfil three crucial roles in social movements:

- **information**: capacity of networks to create opportunities for participation
- **identity**: social ties to 'significant others' create and reproduce solidarity
- **exchange**: informal circulation of social approval, reward and sanctions.

So, alliances and networks lie at the heart of mobilisation and may cross formal organisational, professional and social boundaries. They enable movements to recruit members, obtain resources and disseminate information. The networks of everyday life harbour a multitude of resources which can be tapped into for the purposes of achieving a shared cause. Alinsky (Alinsky, 1972) referred to this as 'schmoozing the community': get to know the people; acquire local knowledge (legends, values, small talk); make friends with leaders of key groups (religious groups, PTAs, consumer groups, clubs, women's groups); search out the leaders; find out what the key issues are (the 'number one' interest); and then build the 'community coalition' focusing on the 90% with which the various groups agree. A lot of this is about the building of alliances, negotiating agreement and trust, by knowing, initially, who are your allies, bedfellows, adversaries and opponents:

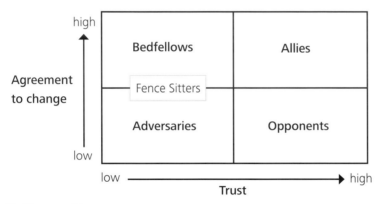

Figure 45: *Alliance matrix*
Negotiating agreement and trust (Block, 1991)

With networks also come leaders; places of association; communication channels; and a stock of organisational and administrative materials. So, for example, the US civil rights movement grew massively in the 1940s and 1950s because it was able to call upon a host of established and new groups to support its cause, including the National Council of Churches; YWCA; the National Association for the Advancement of Coloured People;, Congress of Racial Equality (CORE): Legal Defence and Education Fund; and Martin Luther King's Southern Christian Leadership Conference (McAdam and Scott, 2005).

Wenger and Snyder (Wenger and Snyder, 2000, cited in Bate and Robert, 2002) drew a useful distinction between the types of networks seen in movements and the more traditional 'project team' or 'formal work group' typically seen in healthcare improvement efforts. They use the term 'community of practice' to identify networks that fulfil the three crucial roles of information, identity and exchange:

'Communities of practice'

	Purpose?	Who?	Held together by?	How long?
Communities of practice	To develop members capabilities: to build and exchange knowledge	Members who select themselves	Passion, commitment and identification with the groups expertise	As long as there is interest in maintaining the group
Formal work group	To deliver a product or service	Everyone who reports to the group's manager	Job requirements and common goals	Until the next reorganisation
Project team	To accomplish a specific task	Employees assigned by senior management	The project's milestones and goals	Until the project has been completed
Informal network	To collect and pass on business information	Friends and business acquaintances	Mutual needs	As long as reason to connect exists

Figure 46: The 'community of practice'
Source: E. Wenger and W.M. Snyder, © Harvard Business Review, 1 January 2000, reproduced with permission, 2000

What makes for effective movement leaders?

As well as the first issue addressed in this section (how leadership is organised in a movement), there is also the need to have the right leadership characteristics. These characteristics need to promote the likelihood of action (with minimal bureaucracy and maximum inclusion) by bringing as many people in to the movement as possible:

"Leaders are critical to social movements: they inspire commitment, mobilise resources, create and recognise opportunities, devise strategies, frame demands, and influence outcomes."

Morris & Staggenborg, 2001

Figure 47: *The right leadership characteristics*

So organising for mobilisation not only requires different forms of organisation, strategies and tactics, but also requires leaders in a healthcare context to think:

• 'energy' not efficiency
• 'patient' not organisation
• 'we' not 'I'
• action not planning
• alliances not allegiances.

The specific skills required by a movement leader include articulating the cause for which the movement is striving (see 'positioning' responsibilities earlier in this section). Part of the art of this articulator role lies in making effective use of the mass media. A good example is Candy Lightner who formed the US 'Mothers Against Drunk Drivers' (MADD) after her daughter was killed. She was able to invoke motherhood and victims' rights in her framing of the problem and spurred the movement on with her moral outrage. Such a leader frames for the media, holds press conferences and acts a spokesperson.

Movements leaders also require intellectual skills:

"To be successful, social movements require that a myriad of intellectual tasks be performed extremely well. A host of social movement activities – framing grievances and formulating ideologies, debating, interfacing with media, writing, orating, devising strategies and tactics, creatively synthesising information gleaned from local, national and international venues, dialoguing with internal and external elites, improvising and innovating, developing rationales for coalition building and channelling emotions – are primarily intellectual tasks". (Oberschall, 1973; Ospina and Schall, 2001)

It should also be noted that while, "the early stages of a movement are typically an "orgy of participation and of talk" in which participants share stories, socially construct meaning, and explore new ideas" (Oberschall, 1973; Ospina and Schall, 2001), over time the leadership role will change from constructing a collective identity and enabling participation in collective action at various levels, to setting goals and developing strategies, creating organisations and shaping their structures and forging connections among activists, organisations and levels of action.

7.2.3 Get the strategy right

Having established the leadership model, the next task will be to adopt an effective strategy for the context.

Strategy is all about making choices between alternatives, and these choices pretty well determine failure or success. The choices a movement makes between different strategies, tactics and courses of action will therefore have a major impact upon the direction and success, or otherwise, of the movement. Jasper (Jasper, 2004) has summarised some 23 different choices or dilemmas that movements have to face and we have adapted them slightly into the list here. Not all the dilemmas will apply to every movement (this will depend upon the original aims of the movement and the context in which it is operating). But the list reflects the type of challenges and choices that social movements and their leaders typically come across. There is no single right answer and the core team will need to consider the different choices and options:

1.   *The organisational dilemma.* In what manner and to what degree does the movement need to be organised? How formal/informal should the movement be? Should it be centralised or decentralised? Should it aim to be as efficient in its decision-making as possible, or to be as inclusive and democratic as possible?

2.   *The extension dilemma.* What is the optimum size and scale of the movement? As size increases, so does potential power and influence, yet at the same time the movement becomes susceptible to factionalism and conflict, dilution and problems of co-ordination and control. Choice is not only about size and scale, but also extends to whether mem bership is open or restricted? Which is most appropriate?

3.   *Shifting goals.* Do you stick tenaciously to your original values and goals, or do you react flexibly and opportunistically to the emerging situation? Grasping new opportunities (such as unexpected alliances) can lead to greater movement growth and success, but it can also lead to compromise and limited victories at the cost of more sweeping, ambitious ones.

4.   *Naughty or nice?* To what extent do you work with or against the system? Are you likely to gain more by having people loving you or fearing you?

5.   *The dilemma of inevitability.* How inevitable should you make the success of your cause sound? An approach that suggests you will inevitably win does offer confidence, but makes collective action less critical.

6.   *Direct or indirect moves?* Should you channel your efforts into direct confrontations with opponents, or into indirect moves such as persuading third parties, gathering resources, building networks and so on?

7.   *Plan versus opportunity?* Should you plan initiatives of your own, or watch and wait for opponents to make mistakes?

8.   *The basket dilemma.* Do you aim for one decisive engagement, winner-takes-all, or do you spread your risk over many smaller engagements?

9.   *The dilemma of false arenas.* Do you aim for representation in certain areas, for instance high-profile committees and formal groups, which may take a lot of time without advanc ing your cause?

10.   *Victim or hero?* Do you portray yourself as wronged victim in need of help, or as strong, avenging hero?

11.   *Villain or clown?* Do you portray opponents as a strong and dangerous, or as silly and contemptible?

Figure 48: *Choices and dilemmas faced by movements*

12. *The engagement dilemma.* Should you move from latency and community into active engagement and visibility? The latter course brings a number of risks, such as external repression or misrepresentation and internal conflicts over strategy.

13. *Money's curse.* Do you seek financial support? Money is often seen as dirtying your hands, yet even movements that are 'above' such mundane issues nonetheless depend on financial resources.

14. *The radical-flank dilemma.* Do you adopt extreme words and action? They get attention, and often take opponents by surprise, but they usually play poorly with bystanders and authorities.

15. *The media dilemma.* Do you make use of third party mass media approaches? New media can get your message to broad audiences but, like all powerful allies, they are likely to distort it in doing so.

16. *The bridge-builders dilemma.* How far - and how many - bridges should you seek to build? Individuals who can mediate between groups, or different sides in a conflict, often lose the trust of their own groups by doing so; caught on the horns of reaching out or reaching in.

17. *The familiar and the new.* How innovative and creative should you be? New tactics surprise opponents and authorities, but it is typically hard for your own group to pull them off.

▶ 7.2.4 Get the tactics right

Having set the overall strategy, the next question is what tactics to use, because actions do speaker louder than words! As suggested in the introduction, bringing a social movement perspective to bear on NHS improvement is about doing things differently, rather than just thinking differently. So what are those different ways of doing things?

Movements adopt a range of tactics and again these are influenced by the context in which they are operating. Some movements, such as Greenpeace, have been associated with quite confrontational extreme tactics, whereas others seek to adopt a more consensual approach. Movements typically position themselves and their tactics at a point along the spectrum from moderate, reformist action, to extreme, disruptive action. The choice of tactics depends on:

• whether the movement is predominantly 'issue centered' or 'identity centered'
• whether the external context is friendly or hostile
• how powerful the people are in the group
• how many supporters the movement has
• resources available.

7. ORGANISE FOR IMPACT

At the moderate, reformist end of the spectrum, action tends to be all about awareness raising, facilitating and persuading. These are typically people and groups that believe there is most to be gained by co-operation with the 'authorities'; groups that work inside the 'norms'. At the other extreme are people and groups who believe that extreme tactics are the only way of making progress (Dunphy and Stace's (1988) notion of 'radical times, radical remedies'). Typical tactics are sit-ins, demonstrations, marches, strikes, blockades and illegal actions. However, the majority of movements lie towards the left-hand end - and are mostly unseen and unremarked - typically adopting tactics like boycotts, dramatisations, leafleting, letter writing, campaigns, lobbying, petitions and press conferences (Taylor and Van Dyke, 2004).

Of course, some movements combine both extremes; for example, Greenpeace combines institutional means of influence, such as lobbying and electoral politics, with extra-institutional strategies, such as demonstrations and boycotts.

At times within the NHS, some of the more radical tactics are employed (for instance during a contentious reconfiguration process), but these are unlikely to be the tactics NHS improvement leaders will choose to work with. There are, however, some useful insights to be gained from looking at approaches commonly used in community activism. For example, the Michigan Land Use Institute (MLUI) guide lists a set of tactics, some of which we have already discussed (eg campaigns, spectacle and performance) and some of which are already applied in an NHS organisational context. Others, however (such as strikes and sit-ins) are not. In addition, there are other tactics worth thinking about, such as post-crisis events as a platform to harness energy.

Movement-based tactics include:

• community activism, for instance polling; direct mail marketing; desk drops; canvassing door to door; lobbying at the entrance to the canteen or other communal space; 'club' membership (eg offering some form of accreditation, signing up to a pledge that indicates a shared set of goals); distributing literature; publishing a newsletter or web material; giving community awards; and booths at public events
• campaigns
• 'spectacles', spectaculars and street theatre
• novelties, stunts, gimmicks and dramatisations
• lobbying, voting and petitioning
• single big events
• post-crisis events
• marches, protests and demonstrations
• strikes, boycotts and sit-ins
• insurgency.

Examples of some of the tactics listed would include Greenpeace's campaign against the dumping of Brent Spar's oil storage buoy, a spectacle which changed perceptions of the sea as a limitless waste repository. A further example is the street theatre of the late 1990s and early 2000s anti-globalisation protests which used giant puppets and satirical masks in what Kauffman (Kauffman, 2001) called the 'carnival against capital'. Another much smaller spectacle was the Tuesday afternoon in November 2002 when a group of 50 women of all ages from West Marin, California, lay down naked in a light rain to spell out the word 'PEACE' with their bodies (as a protest against the threat of war against Iraq). A photographer captured the scene from the top of a ladder and the resulting image sped round the world via the internet:

This latter example is a reminder that 'novelties' can be an important tactic too:

> *"New movements in particular depend on novelty in their early days to draw attention to themselves and their cause, especially media attention".* (Koopmans, 1993, 1995)

With regard to 'single big events', it should be noted that most movements have a big historic day somewhere in their history. For example, environmentalism had the 1992 Rio Earth Summit or, earlier, Earth Day 1970 in which 20 million Americans participated to highlight environmental issues. Such events often follow crises or catastrophic incidents, for example the Clean Air Campaign and Act of 1956 followed the London smog of 1952, in which 4000 people died. Protests obviously form part of the tactical repertoire of movements, for example the anti-Vietnam, anti-Iraq war, anti-nuclear protests. The question is, how far can you, and should you, be prepared to go?

> *"McAdam found that the pace and effectiveness of civil rights protests was largely a function of the movement's ability to devise innovative and disruptive tactics that temporarily prove the stalemate between civil rights forces and their segregationist opponents. Lacking sufficient power to defeat Southern segregationists in a local confrontation, insurgents sought, through use of new and provocative tactics - the sit-in, freedom rides, the Freedom Summer project to induce their opponents to disrupt public order to the point where supportive federal intervention was required".*
> (Davis, G.F. and Zald, M, 2005)

The media can also play an important role in movement success or failure. It defines for activists whether they are taken seriously as agents of possible change, it can validate the movement as important, and often rewards novelty, polemic and confrontation. Direct tactics with regard to the media include: cultivating press relations; running advertisements; media appearances; public service announcements; and public relations. Indirect tactics might involve some of the tactics listed above, such as public demonstration, civil disobedience and vigils which in themselves attract media coverage.

Evidence suggests that people in subordinate economic and social positions, and who lack political, organisation or legal access, are more likely to engage in disruptive protest (Scott, 1985; Van Dyke et al, 2001). The less the power you have as a group (for instance, students, ethnic minorities), the more likely you are to (have to) use confrontational tactics (McCarthy and Zald, 1973; Snow et al, 1980; McAdam, 1986; Whyte, 1989; Soule, 1997).

Alinsky's famous 'rules for radicals' (Alinsky, 1972) provide a broader set of guidelines for any movement that may help shape its strategic and tactical choices. To Alinksy, power was about people organising others to exert power collectively, and this meant doing everything you could with your available resources. Alinksy is an archetype for those who view change as a political process. However, while power is what it was all about for Alinksy, organisation was interesting to him as well because power is organised: his simple formula for success was 'agitate, aggravate, educate and organise.'

Rule 1: *Power is not only what you have, but what the enemy thinks you have.*
Power through the senses: if you've got power, then parade it so your enemy can see it. If you've got numbers but no power, think of your ears and make a lot of noise. And if you have got no power and no numbers, the least you can do is make a stink.

Rule 2: *Never go outside the experience of your people.*
If you do they will get confused and fearful and retreat. 'Play at home' – their values, their programmes, their world.

Rule 3: *But wherever possible go outside the experience of your enemy.*
Here you want to cause confusion, fear and retreat. 'Make them play away from home'.

Rule 4: *Make them live up to their own book of rules.*
Which they will never be able to do.

Rule 5: *Ridicule is man's most potent weapon.*
It's almost impossible to counter-attack ridicule, and it also infuriates and flusters your opponent.

Rule 6: *A good tactic is one your people enjoy.*
If your people aren't having a ball doing it, there is something wrong with the tactic.

Rule 7: *A tactic that drags on for too long becomes a drag.*
Strike while the iron is hot; it will soon cool down.

Rule 8 *Keep the pressure on.*
Keep up constant pressure and wear your opponent down by doing lots of different things. Keep them coming, one after another.

Rule 9: *The threat is more terrifying than the thing itself.*

Rule 10: *Unceasing pressure causes an escalation of action and reaction.*
Action causes reaction; further action is the reaction to the reaction, and so on.

Rule 11: *The price of a successful attack is a constructive alternative.*
Be careful not to be trapped by an opponent or interviewer who says, 'You're right, so what would you do?'

Rule 12: *Pick the target, freeze it, personalise it, polarise it.*
Do not try to attack abstract organisations or bureaucracies. Identify a responsible individual. Ignore attempts to shift or spread the blame. Personalise it.

Figure 49: *Saul Alinsky's 'rules for radicals'*

8. KEEP FORWARD MOMENTUM

This fifth and final principle is concerned with the need to keep forward momentum. The first four principles discussed in this document are all necessary, but still not sufficient to successfully bring a movements approach to bear on NHS improvement. By applying the first four principles:

- 'change as a personal mission'
- 'frame to connect with hearts and minds'
- 'energise and mobilise'
- 'organise for impact'.

A movement may have some energy, mass and mobilised people, but the missing key success factor is momentum: put simply, now you've got going, how do you keep going? Momentum is created through building both mass and forward movement, or put another way, through small (or maybe big!) wins:

> *"It's like an ink-blot effect, spreading out from the local focal points of power across the whole country. Once we have our initial successes, the process will gather momen tum and begin to snowball".* (Alinsky, 1972)

As highlighted earlier, the five principles are not part of a sequential, step-by-step process; it is not a case of do the first four principles in order and then begin to pay attention to 'keep forward momentum'. Rather all five principles need to be considered simultaneously and continuously since they are all connected. In other words, 'momentum' is something that you build as you go, not something you only consider at the end (which is how we normally tend to think about sustainability: 'we've moved from point a. to point b., now how do we stay there?').

One way to begin to bring the principles to life is to review a case study of a social movement and to look for signs of the five principles. To illustrate this, we have previously used a timeline of the anti-tobacco campaign - a movement that has just achieved a major breakthrough in England; something no-one would probably have thought possible 10 years, maybe even two years, ago:

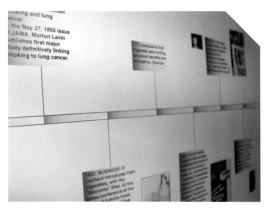

Figure 50: *Anti-tobacco lobby timeline*

Such case studies typically reveal how there are things that can be done as part of all – the first four principles to make sure the momentum is starting to build.

▶ 8.1 Understanding momentum

The term momentum is often used in describing movements.

Momentum and movements go together and is a major preoccupation of people within movements. Whereas NHS improvement leaders typically talk about 'spread and sustainability', movements leaders talk about momentum, which is not a word you hear so much in the NHS. So what is momentum? What metaphors best describe it? Where does it come from? How can it apply to a specific cause?

Momentum can be defined simply as 'how difficult something is to stop'. This is the idea of something that can 'keep going in the absence of external forces'. In other words, the real test that a cause or movement has momentum is that it can survive and grow even in an unreceptive or hostile environment - like a solar cell, it is self-fuelling ('autocatalytic') or 'generative'. The concept is obviously connected to 'sustainability' but needs to be considered in terms of the forward propulsion that keeps the jet-plane in the air - sustainability occurring because of the momentum.

The formal physicist's definition of momentum is that p (momentum) = mass (m) x velocity (v) which, in the case of social movements, means making sure you have sufficient numbers working for your cause (which encompasses issues of recruitment but is mainly about keeping people on board) and achieving things (velocity mainly comes from the accumulation of wins). Momentum needs to be purposefully built as a movement grows; it is not an afterthought, but ultimately the factor that determines whether a cause succeeds or fails.

To understand how to build and maintain momentum, we need to address head on the reasons why we know that some movements lose momentum.

8. KEEP FORWARD MOMENTUM

▶ 8.1.1 Make change a personal mission

A common failure is that people slip back into old ways of thinking and behaviours. The key to preventing this is to focus on transforming people's consciousness so that once they have bought into a new way of thinking, there is no way that they are going to consider going back to the old ways. For example, no-one is now going to say 'apartheid, maybe it wasn't so bad after all'; or 'why don't we bring back smoking on trains and buses'. Achieving this is about moving people to a different way of thinking and then maintaining that shift in consciousness by the 'cause' continuing to be seen as legitimate and effective (ie it must continue to resonate and be plausible). Then people will continue to take personal ownership and responsibility for making change happen.

Another danger sign is when people are unable to see the possibility of success, implying a need for resilience and optimism. Dealing with such dips and spirals of energy is a matter of building relationships and reciprocal commitments to each other. And because it is a social and personal relationship, so it requires face-to-face interaction through events. The emphasis should also be on small informal groups, connected to a loose network, and the resulting 'pull' of commonly-held aspirations, beliefs and social ties with one another (McAdam, 1986). Connectivity is therefore one of the keys to momentum.

▶ 8.1.2 Frame to connect with hearts and minds

Movements can lose momentum because the cause loses resonance or becomes hackneyed in the absence of any perceivable change. It is therefore important to constantly reframe and realign the cause, both to maintain its freshness and relevance with other causes or new initiatives - 'piggy-backing' on other big events, current flavours, fads, fashions and bandwagons. Leaders should be opportunistic in doing this and avoid being hidden away in a tributary somewhere, away from the mainstream. They should be prepared to change their frame (but not their cause) - social movement leaders do this all the time.

▶ 8.1.3 Energise and mobilise

There are a number of failure modes around this principle. Firstly, and quite simply, there is often an issue about a lack of time, so it is important to consider how to create slack in the system so the cause can be pursued. Then, having recruited people to a cause, they need to be retained; in order to do this we need to understand why people initially join movements and, importantly, why they leave. There are many reasons why people remain in a movement, but the main ones are that they feel sufficiently obligated to fellow participants in the 'community' to want to continue to support them; they simply enjoy being with the community; or they see the movement as having a fair chance of success. In essence, people stay because they have partly merged their personal identity with the collective identity of the movement; to walk away would be the same as leaving part of yourself behind. Such collective identity can be constructed through collective events.

The answer to the second question - why do people leave movements - is the flipside of this: they leave it when they feel let down or disappointed with their peers; or simply when the fun goes out of it; or they begin to doubt that it may ever achieve its goals. In 2002, the NHS Modernisation Agency conducted a study into the characteristics of clinicians who had moved from being sceptics

THE POWER OF ONE, THE POWER OF MANY

to improvement champions. The researchers identified a sub-population of sceptics who became improvement champions, but then because their expectations were not met, became sceptics again. They then tended to be more sceptical than the clinicians who had just been sceptics in the first place. There are important lessons here for building the NHS improvement movement. If we want to win clinicians to our cause, we have to take a long-term, self-generating perspective. To minimise the likelihood of people leaving, it is essential to build networks (the things that keep people in movements).

A common feature to emerge as movements evolve, is self-destructive group behaviour which can be in a number of forms (for example, through 'fiefdoms' emerging or corrosive people whose behaviours go unchallenged). Both of these potential failure modes point to the need to manage the politics and avoid factionalism, something best achieved through ensuring connectivity and a shared identity.

8.1.4 Organise for impact

Another failure mode is that there can sometimes be a stand-off between the 'movement' and the wider organisation of which it is a part. This points to the need to work with the system when you can, and to build partnerships by piggybacking, gaining representation on decision-making bodies without being absorbed into them, building relationships, and having a presence with established institutions (explicitly working 'with' rather than 'for' or 'against'). This general approach is reflected in the following quote from one of the members of the Patients Council in North East Manchester (which was one of our four original field test sites):

"We've got a member who started off banging away at the door, knocking and shouting and screaming and when it started he was saying "if we're activists, then we're activists, label it that" but to me what we have done - and this is the key - we could go out with a baseball bat to crack a nut and I think we'd get a lot of publicity for a couple of months and then it will go and nothing would happen ... what we've got to try and do is find a way to work in partnership, not to confront".

Other danger signs under this principle would be if members of the movement are feeling 'left behind', implying that the leaders need to keep in touch and not become a distant elite group. If key leaders or individuals leave the movement, then this may imply a need for shared or distributed leadership. Also, a lack of co-ordination implies a need for an organisational infrastructure to keep the movement going. The starting points of movements - informal groups of friends, ad-hoc committees, or loose associations of activists - are simply not sufficient to develop or maintain a movement. Organisation is required. Evidence shows that campaigns and movements are sustained by a highly- decentralised network of local and regional groups (Rucht and Roose, 2003; McCannon, 2009) and supported at the national level (Hunold, 2001).

Finally, people will soon drop out if nothing happens. So leaders need to maintain energies and loyalties of existing members by working for concrete action and visible victories.

8. KEEP FORWARD MOMENTUM

"Failure is an unpopular subject among social movement scholars. Like death and taxes at social gatherings, it is a topic that many of us avoid. In contrast, the birth of insurgency is eagerly debated. As a result, our theories of movement emergence are much more sophisti cated and convincing than our models of movement development and decline."
(Voss, 1996)

It is a truth that the majority of social movements fail partially or completely; for example, in Gamson's 2004 study of US social movements (Gamson, 2004), he found that over half the organisations in his representative sample failed partially or completely (227). As NHS improvement leaders, we need to be aware of the reasons for these failures so we are best placed to avoid them in our movements.

9. IN CLOSING

That the different set of ideas and approaches to change and improvement described in this report resonate with healthcare staff is not in doubt. In our work with field-test sites it is clear that the generative approach which is central to social movement thinking - with its emphasis on liberating energies and mobilising staff at the grass roots level - does strike a chord with the practitioners:

"I think there's certainly more freedom. I don't mean it's not organised but there's more opportunity to probably think outside of the box and be a bit different."

"With some project deadlines you feel that they are put on you and forced, and I thinkthis is trying to get around all that and being about us wanting to bring about the change ourselves. This isn't the usual "death by project management."

"Well it went from a group that had never met before in January to them wanting to meet in the evenings once a week because they were so enthused about the whole thing. It was incredible how this happened."

"We just talked about things we could do and it was quite infectious. People were saying we could do this, we could do that and the ideas were brilliant."

The challenge remains of how to put this new perspective (and its associated tactics and techniques) into widespread practice in the organisational context of the contemporary NHS.

The NHS Institute is continuing to work with teams from across the NHS in England to distil the knowledge available and translate the powerful concepts and ideas from social movement theory into practical strategies and 'how to' tactics. For example, the learning from the field test sites has been synthesised to develop a two-and-a-half-day training event built around the five principles described in this report. This draws on a rigorous review of the academic literature and the testament of NHS practitioners from the field test sites.

While this process further demonstrated the strength of the ideas and framework, it was found that the training approach itself was highly resource intensive and also inconsistent with the model of spread that had been adopted by the NHS Institute. Additionally, although a highly-successful event, the key weaknesses were that people came with different levels of preparation and that some teams struggled to apply the ideas without more structured follow-up.

Therefore, the need remained to test alternative ways of delivering the approach to practitioners. The nature of the intervention means that the movement approach is not something that can be meaningfully 'taught' in a technical way; rather it is something that has to be experienced, with people using the ideas themselves in order to become competent in facilitating others. This became the key area for testing in the next phase.

Building on this learning, the NHS Institute linked up with improvement leaders from the ten Strategic Health Authorities with the aim of identifying senior change leaders from across the system. Individuals were invited to attend a one-day event with a colleague with a particular cause that they wished to work on using this approach. It was felt that this would support a shared interpretation of the principles and framework, making it easier to translate the learning for their own organisation. The aim was to:

• help participants understand the approaches laid out in the social movement field book; The power of one, the power of many – from intent to impact produced to support the learning activities;
• coach them in the use of a range of tools and techniques for applying social movement thinking to their own 'causes' in their organisations;
• help us gather further evidence around the effectiveness of this change methodology.

Over the next six months, the group was given the opportunity to participate in a range of learning events which included workshops, WebEx activity, organisational coaching and a discussion forum networking space. Eleven of the organisations represented worked closely with Stanton Marris, using the Organisational Energy IndexTM within their organisations. Additionally, in response to direct requests, a number of bespoke events were run, designed and delivered in collaboration with the service.

At the end of that period, the group came together again. Case studies for eight of the eleven organisations who used the Organisational Energy Index™ have been written up. More will follow. This is providing impressive evidence of the effectiveness of the programme and the approach. Quotes from organisations who have embraced social movements include:

"Social movement thinking enables staff to feel they can generate and sustain change. Social movement thinking can help achieve more through harnessing the energy of others."

"The positive impact of social movement thinking can pervade day-to-day communications and approach to strategy."

"Social movement thinking help staff to think of different ways of approaching and enabling change."

Following further prototypes and testing, the Social Movements Field Book is being developed in two versions, each framed for a specific audience:

- a field book for activists
- a field book for leaders.

Included in this second cohort was a team of four staff from the Department of Health who were working on the development of NHS Values. As a direct result of exposure to this thinking, the Department of Health commissioned the NHS Institute to work with local NHS teams, using social movements principles, to co-design, test and deliver a suite of resources. The aim of this work is to enable organisations to develop and embed their values locally in order to bring about large-scale transformational change.

We are now entering a new phase for this work; 'Keeping forward momentum'. This includes:

- establishing a library of social movement literature
- working with senior leadership and activists to co-design reference material for the two new versions of the field book
- the NHS Institute team becoming more of a signposting resource and a support for the establishment of viable networks
- utilising the social movement approach in mainstream strategic planning for large-scale change
- continuing to excite and engage NHS change activists and leaders in this thinking, creating a real force for sustainable change.

In the spirit of a social movement, the NHS Institute would welcome all contributions to this on-going exploration of the potential of social movements thinking to dramatically improve health and healthcare services.

To find out more about Social Movement thinking at the NHS Institute for Innovation and Improvement please contact:

Elizabeth Carter
National Programme Lead, Social Movements
NHS Institute for Innovation and Improvement

Liz.carter@institute.nhs.uk
Tel: 07833 235366

And the NHSI website www.institute.nhs.uk

Appendix 1 - Rocking the boat but not falling out:
the journey of two 'Organisational Radicals'

Debbie Taylor and Steve Allder are an unusual pair. They share an office, they share work, they share confidences and they share an enormous trust and respect for each other. They are unusual because one is a hospital manager, the other a practicing clinician. The most important thing they share is a passion for improving patient care.

Now Head of Service Improvement at Plymouth Hospital NHS Trust, Debbie was a clinical practitioner for 20 years. She left because of her passion for change: *"I got frustrated. I wanted to change things but felt unable to"*. That frustration changed Debbie's trajectory. In 2003, as a new Outpatient Improvement Manager working on the partial booking programme, she had found her niche. By 2005 she had taken up an opportunity to lead service improvement within the Trust. "But I still felt that the work was small-scale. I wanted something big. Then I met Steve, and my life hasn't been the same since!".

Steve is a neurologist. By 2002 he was frustrated with the system of care in which he worked. Recognising the need to change the system led to an interest and then training in clinical systems improvement (CSI) – a data-rich, whole-systems approach to analysing and improving the processes of care. Steve took the position of Clinical Director of Neuroscience in 2005. In his new role, he became aware of Debbie's work and that of her service improvement team. Steve and Debbie quickly realised that, despite their different professional backgrounds, they spoke the same language.

This meeting of hearts and minds began a journey of impact and learning that has proved both rewarding and personally challenging. *"The last two years have been the most stimulating but also the most challenging, ever"* (Steve). In the language of social movements, Steve and Debbie are "Organisational Radicals": people who take action in line with their strong convictions, who are different from the traditional majority yet working within the system, not against it.
"You need to learn how to agitate for change, to be 'subversive' whilst not being sidelined" (Steve)

A shared cause

Debbie and Steve share the same cause: to improve patient experience and clinical outcomes for the people of Plymouth. They are both committed to using systems thinking and clinical systems improvement as an over-arching approach to achieving this aim. Their first major challenge on this journey came in August 2006.

Unbeknown to him at the time, when Steve took on the role of Clinical Director, he also effectively took on responsibility for delivering £l million of savings. The first tangible sign for Steve of potential financial crisis in the Trust was hearing that wards would have to be closed. At a Board Meeting focused on the growing crisis, it dawned on him that there was a huge gap between the Executives and the Medical leadership, a gap that needed to be bridged.

It was also clear that the finances "didn't add up" and that something more fundamental had to change. Steve recognised that there was a potential 'win-win' opportunity if a service redesign and improvement approach could be secured. But it needed real clinical engagement and leadership. *"At that point, I decided to get involved. I didn't realise at the time just how stressful this kind of change is"*. Steve spent that weekend working on the data. His analysis showed that the Trust could take 300 beds out of the system if it properly redesigned its services. The scene was set for the first stage of Debbie and Steve's journey. They both believed they could make the necessary changes to significantly reduce the bed count while improving quality of services. But they also understood they needed to "create the engagement with clinical staff which we would need for the next ten years of the journey".

Framing to connect with people's hearts and minds

The approach of the team has sometimes rubbed up against the prevailing performance-driven culture within the organisation. A key challenge has been how to convince those who do not have a deep understanding of systems thinking and the power of data to inform strategic decisions. *"It's very difficult to find yourself in a leadership position but with no real power"*. (Debbie)

Steve's expertise as a neurologist has helped address this. Thinking about the role of conscious and unconscious thought and the fact that in most interactions, the unconscious is largely at play, helped Steve recognise that the only person you can definitely change is yourself. *"So in an interaction, I ask myself 'is my behaviour aligned to what I want to achieve?' and that way have got better at managing myself"* (Steve). The insight has led to a greater understanding of the importance of "framing" messages for other people in ways that will influence their behaviour. Finding ways to connect with different people's emotional and / or rational thinking has helped to bring others with them. In particular, the team recognise the need to frame "target driven" work in terms of what it means for patients and for clinicians.

Debbie and Steve have also used framing to help themselves keep focused on the journey. They have found it helpful to have an explicit personal agenda and to keep asking *"how does this fit with what I want?"*. For Steve, his over-arching cause is *'to ensure the success of the NHS'*. That has sometimes meant re-framing difficulties: *"maybe we can't make it happen in this Trust, at this time, but we can use the experience"*.

Energising and mobilising others

Using their joint expertise and experience in CSI and the skills and energy of the service improvement team, Steve and Debbie have helped the Trust make significant improvements to services. Their initial work has produced measurable outputs, including a significantly reduced bed count, improved quality indicators, and improved A&E performance. With these results, their approach has gained recognition and they have been increasingly asked to take on more challenges, including the 18-week referral to treatment target.

Building on their initial experience, the team have also found that crises, rather than always being negative, can provide rich opportunities for change. *"Crises create energy for change. With the 4-hour target it needed several crises to shift people to doing what they needed to do"* (Steve).

Debbie and Steve have used the power of CSI, combined with social movement thinking, to engage and mobilise clinical teams. Staff have begun to take on work themselves, pulling on the service improvement team as a resource. *"It's very powerful to have analysis and evidence – that's a key hook for clinicians. But keeping them hooked is different. We needed to get them involved, to work with them and get them doing some analysis themselves."* (Debbie)

> *"It got to a point where people were engaging – they wanted to know more. Once you mobilise people, things move even if you stand still."* (Steve)

Organising for impact

Mainstreaming the knowledge and skills inherent in service improvement has always been a focus for Debbie and Steve. They recognise that not only do they need to inform and energise key leaders and clinicians around the work but that they need to organise themselves to maximise impact across the organisation. To this end, the team is focusing on different aspects of work that all contribute to their cause.

The Trust's four Clinical Systems Improvement engineers (all qualified doctors) and the Service Improvement Team are working directly with the frontline to redesign services, while Debbie provides guidance and support. Along with external expert, Dr Kate Silvester, they are helping to build systems knowledge and capability among frontline staff. Meanwhile, Steve is focusing upwards, working with the Director of Human Resources to develop capability among directors and senior managers. In addition, the team are partnering with a new operational manager, focusing on the 18-week target work, while the Service Improvement Team is expanding to embrace the work and expertise of the Trust's Productive Ward facilitators.

All are intent on ensuring that clear data, information and analysis support the Trust's strategic direction. The team is now providing 'dash-boards' of information for senior leaders on both the 4-hour and 18-week targets to enable clear decision-making.

But perhaps the most visible signal that Debbie and Steve's approach is really reaching the mainstream is a request from the chief executive that they produce an "enabling strategy" on the CSI approach for the Trust's integrated business plan for 2009.

Learning from Social Movements

In early 2008, Debbie and Steve joined a second phase of the NHS Institute's experimental work on Social Movements.

Attending the first workshop in March, Debbie and Steve suddenly felt at home: *"When we opened the ['Social Movement Handbook'], we realised we could have written it. We said 'this is us!'. We've got a team of six on Level 7, but we're trying to change the world... The workshops began to help put into context some of what we'd been doing over the past couple of years".* (Debbie)

As well as providing some external validation of their approach and thinking, the team found that the workshops also gave them some "nudges" and direction from different angles. For example, they found insights on framing a cause and its messages to connect with its different audiences particularly helpful.

"We'd been doing CSI, with lots of technical analysis and so on, but the hearts and minds stuff has been the icing on the cake". (Debbie)

The regular group events within the programme have provided the additional benefit of encouraging the team to keep reflecting on and synthesising their learning in order to share with others.

Change as a personal mission

Both Debbie and Steve acknowledge that the journey has been hard so far. *"You can suddenly see how [transformational change] can eat you up if you're not careful."* (Steve)

Debbie, as a manager, has found that it can be hard to achieve change on your own. A key difficulty has been *"the constant challenge, having to justify yourself. You have to build credibility. For managers this can be more difficult. There are many occasions when I've wondered, 'why do I continue?' "*.

One of Steve's particular survival strategies is to constantly raid the literature on change management and on how to approach things laterally within an organisation. Not only has this strategy provided important insights and lessons but it has also helped to make sense of personal experiences, particularly the difficult ones: *"Understanding Peter Senge was life-saving!"* (Steve).

The work of Peter Senge, in his book, The Fifth Discipline, describes systems dynamics and discusses the set of "limiting conditions" that can make change so difficult within any system. *"This made me realise why this type of change is so difficult and then helped me see what I needed ot work on".* Senge also shows how change cannot be created through "push" strategies, and that if we resist this natural tendency, people begin to "pull", a lesson that Debbie and Steve have seen work in practice.

Steve also found that one particular line from the book, 'Leadership on the line', by Heifetz and Linsky, really resonated with his experience: "If you are going to lead adaptive change, you will be attacked, marginalised, subverted and seduced". His supportive medical director reinforced this insight, telling Steve that if he was going to change things, he should expect challenge, sometimes very painful, from others. Realising that such challenge is nothing personal, but rather the nature of leading transformational change, has been an important insight and one that has helped Steve get through the tough times.

This strategy of turning to the literature has also led to a realisation that no single approach has all the answers and that 'promiscuity' is a better tactic when it comes to change. Although CSI is the core improvement technique used by the team, they have been open to a range of other approaches, using insights from lean thinking and the model for improvement as well as social movements to further their cause.

Both Debbie and Steve are strongly committed to their cause and prepared to make sacrifices in order to achieve it. But they know that there are limits to what they can achieve alone and have recognised what is important in keeping them "afloat".

"You have to know what your 'moments of truth' are; what are your limits before you have to get out to preserve your values and philosophy." (Steve)

Keeping afloat as an Organisational Radical: key insights

1. Keep 'the patient' and your overall cause central to everything you do

2. Find others who share your passion

3. Do not get too attached to one technique or approach – use any that will contribute to your cause

4. Seek out links between other people's causes and your own, then build bridges to maximise leverage

5. Actively build support networks you can rely on – colleagues, fellow activists, external consultants, mentors

6. Hold on – something will always emerge to get you to the next stage of the journey

7. Look ahead and keep the big picture in mind to help you maintain perspective

8. Be brave! Meaningful change requires courage and tenacity, but the rewards can be great.

Keeping forward momentum

The journey is not yet over, far from it. For both Steve and Debbie, a key insight gained from their work and personal experience so far is that spreading and sustaining this kind of change means they are in it for the long haul. *"If you want to create transformational change, it's going to take a long time. If you push it, you won't really change anything. The time lines have to be much longer. You need to be constantly vigilant and adapting."* (Steve).

But although this knowledge requires tenacity, it also provides hope. Steve has learned to keep going despite seemingly intractable challenges: *"You just need to hold on and something unexpected will always happen to get you to the next stage"*. That learning has been reinforced time and again when Debbie and Steve have reached points at which it seemed impossible to keep going forward.

This duo certainly knows how to rock the boat…but they are determined to stay in it for the reward: achieving real improvements for patients.

FOOTNOTE:

Since this article was written, Steve has resigned from his post as Clinical Director for Service Improvement. This is largely because he feels that the limiting conditions at an organisational level are currently insurmountable. Both Steve and Debbie are still passionate about their cause but are choosing their battles, with Steve deciding to focus his efforts on the elements where he can have maximum impact and influence. His decision reiterates one of the many lessons he has learned about being an organisational radical:

> *"You have to know what your 'moments of truth' are: what are your limits before you have to get out to preserve your values and philosophy".*

Appendix 2 - Energising Conversations
Case Study: Poole Hospital

Poole Hospital NHS Foundation Trust have brought social movement thinking into an innovative approach to engaging with staff.

In June 2007, members of the Trust learned about "Listening into Action": a new approach to engaging with staff and enabling group conversations that lead to action. The Trust was one of 12 pilot sites established to use staff conversations to explore frontline views on values within the NHS prior to the NHS Strategic Review. Later that month, forty members of staff attended a Listening into Action event, led by the Trust's Chief Executive, entitled "staff conversation on NHS values".

> **Poole Hospital NHS Foundation Trust:**
>
> - 784 beds
> - Trauma centre for East Dorset
> - High elderly population
> - 85% workload = emergency unplanned care
> - High levels of staff and patient satisfaction

The session surfaced issues that were affecting morale, productivity and patient care. It resulted in a local action plan to reduce bureaucracy, increase staff autonomy and demonstrate the Trust's commitment to valuing its staff by involving them fully in the re-design of priority services. Feedback from the event contributed to a wider report on NHS values, while local staff felt more appreciated and influential as a result of being actively listened to.

"This Trust event went very well, with staff participating fully and giving their views on values within the Trust and their importance to staff and patients. We were impressed by the levels of energy shown and were determined to respond to the views and suggestions of the participants" - Barbara Peddie Associate Director of Operations

> **Listening into Action:**
>
> - Facilitated "Staff Conversations"
> - 2-hour structured session
> - Up to 4 well-framed questions posed to staff
> - Group discussions to surface responses
> - Key points fed back from each group
> - Active listening by leaders
> - Plans made to take action on staff feedback
> - Promises kept

A personal mission

Following the event, two members of the Trust, Marion Seddon and Barbara Peddie, attended a three-day, intensive workshop run by the NHS Institute for Innovation and Improvement. The workshop aimed to expose frontline staff to the concepts and application of Social Movement thinking. Marion, a Matron, and Barbara, the Associate Director of Operations, both worked within the Trust's Surgical Clinical Care Group. They realised this was an approach which could fully exploit the potential of staff conversations and achieve active engagement and mobilisation of a large number of staff in improving patient care.

> "[I feel] excited, motivated, challenged but looking forward to taking back the ideas, concepts – as a different way to looking at change" Marian Seddon (feedback on the workshop)

Despite some reservations about being able to translate the principles of social movements into practice, Barbara and Marion were keen to find a way to apply the approach within their own organisational context.

Finding a cause

Barbara and Marian identified a focused but crucial cause on which to try out their new learning. Badbury Ward was a short-stay surgical unit. In reality, the ward needed to operate on a seven day basis but, with funding for only five, the weekends had to be covered by bank and agency staff. Quality of care was suffering and the sickest patients were being moved to other wards each Friday. Their cause was clear: re-defining Badbury Ward as a full, seven-day facility and eliminating the poor standards of care at weekends. Although some staff were worried or sceptical about participating in a Listening into Action event, the Badbury Ward team were passionate about wanting to address the issues they recognised as impacting detrimentally on the experience of both patients and staff.

Framing for success

One of the many aspects of social movement thinking that resonated with Barbara and Marian was the idea "framing" an issue in a way that makes it meaningful to the target audience. This concept enabled them to articulate their own cause in ways that connected with different stakeholders, by answering the questions, "why should I be involved?" and "what's in it for me?". Key stakeholders they needed to bring on board included senior managers who could make decisions about funding and the clinical staff who were central to bringing about improvements to care.

Prior to undertaking the Badbury "staff conversation", Barbara and Marian produced a carefully framed briefing paper for the Chief Executive, outlining the concepts of social movement thinking and the potential value of using the approach to help improve Bradbury Ward. Through a follow-up face-to-face discussion, they secured her support for their cause, with the proviso that they could demonstrate its alignment with the Trust's philosophy and strategic objectives. The concept of framing also helped them prepare for the staff conversation. Carefully crafted questions and bringing in patients' experiences were crucial to helping build up a picture from many different perspectives and enabling team members to contribute their ideas.

Releasing energy and mobilising action

The Badbury Ward event allowed strong feelings to emerge, particularly around the double standards of care. These were summed up in a poem about a "ward of two dimensions" written by a member of staff who had been a patient on the ward and experienced first-hand the difference between week-day and weekend care.

To help galvanise action from the staff conversations, the Badbury team also invited the Director of Operations to come and work on the ward on a Friday – the most fraught day of the week for staff and patients. This enabled her to experience first-hand the effects of the five-day funding situation on patient care and staff morale. The case was a compelling one and the team gained her support.

Organising for impact

However, Barbara and Marion recognised that getting staff fired up was not enough. They also needed to generate pace and momentum through structured support and planning. A paper by Matron and the Director of Operations for the Trust Board was key to translating ideas into reality. This made the case for change, outlining the key quality issues relating to Badbury, the solutions generated by staff and a financial assessment. When the Board responded with renewed funding for the full seven-day staffing requirements, the Badbury Ward team not only saw demonstrable results from the approach but felt valued and listened to.

> "The most important aspect of the approach seemed to be the generation of change from the grass roots upwards. This would enable more energy, drive and commitment to be demonstrated in order to tackle the problems that need to be addressed."
> - Marian Seddon, Matron

Key points for success:

- Organisation and preparation – a structured approach gets results
- Get the right people in the room – enable people to attend sessions
- Connect with people emotionally – use stories from patients and staff
- Craft questions well – to generate rich and purposeful discussion
- Frame appropriately – use different approaches for different groups
- Go with the energy – others will come on board
- Try things out on a small scale – early success builds momentum
- Responsive leaders are crucial – be prepared to take negative feedback as well as positive

---

Increasing the momentum

With an early success behind them, the team focused on mobilising a wider mass of Trust staff in improving quality of services and identified three further teams that would benefit from the approach. Learning from the impact of getting the Director of Operations personally involved in the cause for Badbury Ward, they sought opportunities to draw in other key leaders. The Performance Management Team and the Human Resources and Training Department were invited to help lead staff conversations around key frontline causes. The strategy worked. Initial scepticism of the approach from the Performance Management Team transformed into strong support, resulting in that team now leading a series of Trust-wide staff conversation events.

Increasing the Momentum

Elective Admissions Team: Improving the Admissions Process

- Invited Performance Management Team to support the process
- Involved a patient to explain issues and problems with admissions
- Resulted in a slicker admissions process
- Moved the Performance Management Team from sceptics to converts of the approach

Trauma Admissions Unit: Developing a Joint Philosophy of Care

- Involved the Human Resources and Training department
- Focused on views from managers and nurses
- Generated agreement on philosophy of care and working as a team
- Enabled clear action on improving the working of the ward and communication

Day Surgery Theatres Team: Dealing with Workload and Capacity

- Key issues relating to relationships, accountability and work style
- Enabled a shift from seeing problems with others to taking ownership and responsibility
- Action plans being developed

Trust-wide Events: Improving Communication with Staff and Achieving 15 Week Target

- Engaged staff from all over the organisation including senior clinicians, managers and members of Trust Board
- Led by Performance Management Team
- Focused on what worked well in the past and how to move forward
- Produced a staff involvement strategy and actions on improving waits

---

Light many fires

The Listening into Action technique provides an innovative approach to engaging with frontline staff on issues important to them. Injecting social movement thinking into the technique, however, has enabled the Poole Hospital team to transform its potential. Using a philosophy of "light many fires", they rapidly built momentum and have harnessed the energy, passion and commitment of staff to improving patient care.

> *"Since implementing this approach we have enjoyed our most successful year so far. Rated excellent by the Healthcare Commission for the quality of service, we are in the top 57 most improved NHS organisations and we continue to meet and exceed targets and reduce hospital acquired infection. I believe that we have been enabled to release our full potential and the impact on improvement to the quality of care we offer our patients is very evident"* Sue Sutherland, Chief Executive

References

Alinsky, S. (1972), Rules for radicals. A pragmatic primer for realistic radicals, New York, Vintage Books.

Bate, S.P. (2004), 'The role of stories and storytelling in organisational change efforts', Intervention Research. International Journal on Culture, Organisation and Management, 1 (1): pp. 27-42.

Bate, S.P. (2005), 'Ethnography with "attitude": mobilising narratives for public sector change'. In M. Veenswijk (Ed.) Organising innovation: new approaches to cultural change and intervention in public sector organisations, Amsterdam, IOS Press.

Bate, S.P. and Robert, G. (2002), 'Knowledge management and communities of practice in the private sector: lessons for modernising the National Health Service in England and Wales', Public Administration, 80 (4): pp. 643-663.

Bate, S.P. and Robert, G. (2007), Bringing user experience to healthcare improvement: the concepts, methods and practices of experience-based design, Oxford, Radcliffe Publishing.

Bate, S.P. and Robert, G. (2009), 'Bringing social movement theory to health care practice and the English national health service'. In J. Banaszak-Holl, S.R. Levitsky, and M. Zald (Eds.) Social movements and the transformation of US health care, Oxford, Oxford University Press. (2009)

Bate, S.P., Bevan, H. and Robert, G. (2004), Towards a million change agents. A review of the social movements literature: implications for large-scale change in the NHS, Leicester, NHS Modernisation Agency.

Bate, S.P., Robert, G. and Bevan, H. (2004), 'The next phase of healthcare improvement: what can we learn from social movements?', Quality and Safety in Healthcare, 13 (1): pp. 62-66.

Bate, S.P., Mendel, P. and Robert, G. (2008), Organising for Quality: the improvement journeys of leading hospitals in Europe and the United States, Oxford, Radcliffe Publishing.

Beckhard, R. and Harris, R. T. (1977), Organizational transitions: managing complex change, Reading MA, Addison Wesley.

Bevan, H. (2007), 'On Organisational energy', Health Service Journal 25 January 2007

Bevan, H. (2007b), 'On Organisational radicals', Health Service Journal 7 February 2007

Berwick D. (2003), 'Improvement, trust and the healthcare workforce', Quality and Safety in Healthcare, 12 (6): pp. 448-452.

Bruch H. and Ghoshal, S. (2003), 'Unleashing organizational energy', MIT Sloan Management Review, 45 (1): pp. 45-51.

Brulle, R. J. (2000), Agency, democracy and nature: the U.S. environmental movement from a critical theory perspective, Cambridge, MIT Press.

Buchanan, D., Ketley, D., Gollop, R., Jones, J.L., Lamont, S., Sharpe, A., Whitby, E. (2002), No going back; a review of the literature on sustaining strategic change, Leicester, NHS Modernisation Agency.

Campbell, J. (1994), The hero with a thousand faces, Princeton NJ, Princeton University Press.

Castells, M. (1997), The power of identity: the information age - economy, society and culture, (Volume 2), Oxford, Blackwell.

Charon R. (1993). 'The narrative road to empathy'. In H. Spiro (Ed) Empathy and the medical profession: beyond pills and the scalpel, New Haven, Yale University Press.

CLEAR IMPACT Consulting Group. (1999), 'Organisational energy audit', http://www.clear-impact.com/energyaudit.htm (accessed 29/01/09).

Davis, G.F. and Zald, M. (2005). 'Social change, social theory and the convergence of movements and organizations'. In G. Davis, D. McAdam, R. Scott and M Zald (Eds.) Social movements and organization theory, Cambridge, Cambridge University Press.

Department of Health. (2000). The NHS Plan, London, HMSO.

Department of Health. (2006). Chief executive's report to the NHS: June 2006, London, HMSO.

Department of Health. (2008). High Quality Care for All: NHS next stage review final report, London, HMSO.

Cottham, H. and Leadbeater, C. (2004). RED Paper 01 Health: co-creating services, London, The Design Council.

Disney, J.L. and Gelb, J. (2000). 'Feminist organizational "success": the state of U.S. women's movement organizations in the 1990s', Women and Politics, 21 (4): pp. 39-76.

Dunphy, D.C. and Stace, D.A. (1988), 'Transformational and coercive strategies for planned organizational change: beyond the OD model', Organization Studies, 9 (3): pp. 317-334.

Gamson, W.A. (2004). 'Bystanders, public opinion and the media'. In D.A. Snow, S.A. Soule, and H. Kriesi (Eds.) The Blackwell companion to social movements, London, Blackwell.

Ganz, M. (2003). 'Resources and resourcefulness: leadership, strategy and organization in the unionization of California agriculture (1959-1966)'. In J. Goodwin and J.M. Jasper (Eds.) Social movement reader: cases and concepts, London, Blackwell.

Gladwell, M. (2002). The tipping point: how little things can make a big difference, Boston MA, Back Bay Books.

Goldstone, J.A. (2001). 'Toward a fourth generation of revolutionary theory', Annual Review of Political Science, 4: pp. 139-87.

Gore, A. (1993). 'From red tape to results: creating a government that works better and costs less', http://govinfo.library.unt.edu/npr/library/nprrpt/annrpt/redtpe93/ (accessed 29/01/09).

Hamel, G. (2006). The future of management, Watertown MA, Harvard Business School Press.

Hamel, G. (2009). 'Moon Shots for Management', Harvard Business Review, February. pp. 91-95

Hay Group. http://www.haygroup.com/ww/About/Index.asp?id=495 (accessed 29/01/09). Healthcare Commission. (2008). National NHS staff survey, 2007, London, Healthcare Commission.

Hirschhorn, L. and May, L. (2000). 'The campaign approach to change: targeting the university's scarcest resources', Change, 32 (3): pp. 30-37.

Huy, Q.N. (1999). 'Emotional capability, emotional intelligence and radical change', Academy of Management Review, 24 (2): pp. 325-345.

Jasper, J.M. (2004). 'A strategic approach to collective action: looking for agency in social-movement choices', Mobilisation, 9 (1): pp. 1-16.

Johnson, B. (1992). Polarity management: identifying and managing unsolvable problems, Amherst MA, Human Resources Development Press.

Kelman, S. (2005). Unleashing change. A study of organizational renewal in government, Washington DC, Brookings Institution Press.

Kleiner, A. (1996). The age of heretics: heroes, outlaws and the forerunners of corporate change, New York, Currency and Doubleday.

Kling, J. (1995). 'Narratives of possibility: social movements, collective stories and the dilemmas of practice'. Paper presented at the 'New social movement and community organising conference', (University of Washington School of Social Work, November 1-3, 1995).

Koopmans, R. (1993). 'The dynamics of protest waves: West Germany, 1965 to 1989', American Sociological Review, 58: pp. 637-58.

Koopmans, R. (1995). Democracy from Below, Boulder CO, Westview Press.

Kotter, J. (2002). The heart of change. Real life stories of how people change their organizations, Watertown MA, Harvard Business School Press.

Leslie, K., Loch, M.A. and Schaninger, W. (2006). 'Managing your organization by the evidence', The McKinsey Quarterly, 3: pp. 65–75.

Loehr, J. and Schwartz, T. (2003). 'The power of full engagement', Sloan Management Review

McAdam, D. (1986). 'Recruitment to high-risk activism: the case of Freedom Summer', American Journal of Sociology, 92: pp. 64-90.

McAdam, D. and Snow, D.A. (1997). Social movements: readings on their emergence, mobilisation and dynamics, Los Angeles, Roxbury.

McAdam, D., Tarrow, S. and Tilly, C. (1995). 'To map contentious politics', Mobilisation, 1 (1): pp. 17-34

McAdam, D. and Scott, W.R. (2005). 'Organizations and movements'. In G.F. Davis, D. McAdam, W.R. Scott and M.N. Zald (Eds.) Social Movements and Organization Theory, New York, Cambridge University Press.

McCannon, C.J. (2008). 'Reflections on dissemination: four years of learning about campaigns and large scale improvement'. Presentation at the 'Institute for Healthcare Improvement national forum', (IHI, December 8, 2008).

McCannon, C.J. (forthcoming). The unprecedented network: a possible future for healthcare improvement in the USA, (under review/unpublished).

McCannon, C.J., Schall, M. and Perla, R.J. (forthcoming). Planning for scale: a guide for designing large-scale improvement initiatives, (under review/unpublished).

McCarthy, J. and Zald, M. (1973). 'Resource mobilization and social movements: a partial theory', The American Journal of Sociology, 82 (6): pp. 1212-1241.

Marwell, G., Oliver, P.E. and Prahl, R. (1988). 'Social networks and collective action: a theory of the critical mass. III', American Journal of Sociology, 94: pp. 502-534.

McConnell, C. (2003). Change activist: make big things happen fast, Harlow, Pearson Education Ltd.

Meyer, D.S. and Tarrow, S. (1998). The social movement society: contentious politics for a new century, Lanham, MD, Rowman Littlefield.

Meyerson, D.E. (2001). 'Radical change, the quiet way', Harvard Business Review, October: pp. 32-40.

Michigan Land Use Institute (unknown). 'Activist toolkit', http://mlui.org/toolkit.asp (accessed 29/01/09).

Morgan, G. (1996). Images of organization. New York, Sage.

Morris, A. and Staggenborg, S. (2002). 'Leadership in social movements', http://www.sociology.north western.edu/faculty/morris/docmorris-leadership.pdf (accessed 29/01/09).

NHS Institute for Innovation and Improvement. (2007). The power of one, the power of many. Becoming an activist: intent to impact. Guide, Warwick, NHS Institute.

NHS Institute. (2008). 'Time and motion. A programme for efficiency in the NHS. HSJ productive series', http://www.hsj.co.uk/images/081106-productive-ward_tcm11-1912299.pdf (accessed 29/01,09).

NHS Institute. (2008). 'The NHS sustainability guide', http://www.institute.nhs.uk/sustainability_model/ introduction/find_out_more_about_the_guide.html (accessed 29/01/09).

NHS Institute. (2009). 'Experienced Based Design: Using patient and staff experience to design better healthcare services', Warwick, NHS Institute

Oberschall, A. (1973). Social conflict and social movements, New Jersey, Prentice-Hall.

Ospina, S.M. and Scall, E. (2001). 'New lenses on leadership'. Presented at the '23rd annual research conference of the Association for Public Policy and Management, (Washington DC, November 1-3, 2001).

Petit-Zeman, S. (2005). Doctor, what's wrong? Making the NHS human again, Abingdon, Routledge.

Platt, G. and Lilley, S.J. (1994). 'Multiple images of a charismatic; an interpretive conception of Martin Luther King, Jr.'s leadership'. In G.M. Platt and C. Gordon (Eds), Self, collective behavior, and society: essays honoring the contributions of Ralph H. Turner, contemporary studies in sociology: theoretical and empirical monographs (volume 12), Greenwich Connecticut, JAI Press.

Rao, H., Monin, P. and Durand, R. (2001). Identity movements and the redefinition of social identity: why French chefs abandoned classical cuisine for nouvelle cuisine, (unpublished manuscript).

Rock, D and Schwartz, J (2009). 'The Neuroscience of Leadership: Strategy and Business'. Booz and Company

Shepherd, H. (1975). 'Rules of thumb for change agents', OD Practitioner, 7 (3): pp. 1-5.

Snow, D.A. and R.D. Benford. (1988). 'Ideology, frame resonance and participant mobilization', International Social Movement Research, 1: pp. 197-219.

Snow, D.A., Soule, S.A. and Kriesi, H. (2004). 'Mapping the terrain'. In D.A. Snow, S.A. Soule and H. Kriesi (Eds.) The Blackwell companion to social movements, Oxford, Blackwell.

Snow, D., Zurcher, L. and Ekland-Olson, S. (1980). 'Social networks and social movements: a microstructural approach to differential recruitment', American Sociological Review, 45: pp. 787-801.

Soule, S.A. (1997). 'The student divestment movement in the United States and the shantytown: diffusion of a protest tactic,' Social Forces, 75 (3): pp. 855-883.

Stanton Marris Ltd. (2009). 'Organisational Energy Index™', www.stantonmarris.com (accessed 29/01/09).

Strang, D. and Jung, D-Il. (2002). 'Organisational change as an orchestrated social movement; determinants and implications of recruitment to a "quality initiative"'. Paper presented at 'Social movement and organisation theory' conference, Michigan, Ann Arbor.

Taylor, V. and van Dyke, N. (2004). 'Get up, stand up: tactical repertoires of social movements. In D.A. Snow, S.A. Soule and H. Kriesi (Eds.) The Blackwell companion to social movements, Oxford, Blackwell.

Voss (1996) "The Collapse of a Social Movement: The Interplay of Mobilizing Structures, Framing, and Political Opportunities in the Knights of Labor." In Comparative Perspectives on Social Movements: Political Opportunities, Mobilizing Structures, and Cultural Framings. Doug McAdam, John McCarthy, and Mayer Zald, eds. New York: Cambridge University Press.

Wenger, E. and Snyder, W.M. (2000). 'Communities of practice: the organisational frontier', Harvard Business Review, Jan–Feb: ff. 139.

Whyte, D. (1994). The heart aroused - poetry and the preservation of the soul in corporate America, New South Wales, Currency.

Zald, M.N. and McCarthy, J.D. (1987). Social movements in an organisational society: collected essays, New Brunswick, NJ, Transaction.

ACKNOWLEDGEMENTS

Partners and partner organisations who have helped us to produce this book

PA Consulting

Optimise

Sarah Garrett

Annabelle Scarfe – Change-fx

Chris Townley